Jarry and Me

The Autobiography of Alfred Jarry

by Oakley Hall III

René Georges Hermann-Paul made this sketch of Alfred Jarry in 1897, a year after the première of *Ubu Roi* scandalized and energized Parisian theatre

The author circa 1974, when he was a student at Boston University and developing his fascination with Jarry

Photographer unknown; reproduction courtesy of Barbara Hall

"Is this Alfred Jarry finally writing Oakley Hall III's autobiography or the other way around? It reads — magnificently — as both at the same time, thus as another instance of that hidden wisdom: we are never only one, but always the occasion of many. Maybe it is Ubu himself fondling the hen, I mean holding the pen? Was there ever pathos in 'Pataphysics? If not, here it is: one bridge further, Oakley Hall III is at it again, biosplicing his & Jarry's life in the theater and Jarry and his theater in life. You are hereby introduced into the Hall of Post-'Pataphysics."

Prof. Pierre Joris
author of *Poasis* and *A Nomad Poetics*

"This is a very strange outlandish book, standing far outside the fenced-in area of the usual literary experiences. It purports to be non-fiction, and is non-fiction, but may have passages which are not entirely veracious, for which however the author is not responsible. Out of two lives, in two different epochs — his own crash-and-burn path as a dramatist in New York, and Alfred Jarry's brief self-destructive career as a surrealist playwright in Paris at the turn of the twentieth century — Oakley Hall has constructed a grand dissonance."

Louis B. Jones
Author, most recently, of *California's Over*

JARRY AND ME

The Autobiography of Alfred Jarry

by Oakley Hall III

FIRST EDITION
SEPTEMBER 2010
COPYRIGHT ©2010 OAKLEY HALL III

PRINTED IN THE UNITED STATES OF AMERICA
ISBN 978-0-9774214-5-9

Absintheur Press
WWW.ABSINTHEURPRESS.COM

Dedicated to Oakley Hall,
Oakley Hall III's father.
He died,
after living well.
Bless him.

With gratitude to Sands Hall,
Oakley Hall III's sister,
who never left her brother for dead
even when he looked and acted the part,
and whose enthusiasm inspired him
to finish this book.

For Hadiya.

Alfred Jarry. Born 1873, presumably of the union of M. and Mme Jarry. One feels that He was born with his Caporal, the Three-pointed moustache He made popular. There was also nothing about His Birth that made one think: Here is a, well, Star.

His UBU Plays, which are best known, were started in High School, and were based on a fellow-student's EB Plays. But UBU is UBU. His mother left His father, allegedly for No Reason, and went to Paris, taking with her Alfred and his sister: Older, undistinguished. Alfred is living with His mother, and becoming Known: for his Three-Directional Moustache and his Addiction to Absinthe. And his UBU plays. And bear in mind this is in 1890-1895: The emergence and description of Surrealism were 20 years in the Future. But that is what Jarry was: a Pre-Surrealist, Absinthiated.

A kind of worship of Jarry by Mme Rachilde, a very popular novelist, also married to Jarry's Editor. Breton, who wrote *The Surrealist Manifesto* in 1924, and Antonin Artaud, who took over Artistic Directorship of the Theatre Alfred Jarry, after Jarry was long dead, were both Surrealists. Both knew Him. Picasso too.

Jarry died 1907. Sort of unmourned, and that's too bad.

I, Oakley Hall III, am an author and playwright. I've translated all three of Alfred Jarry's UBU plays, and staged UBU REX in New York City and at our Lexington Conservatory Theatre, in Lexington, New York, where I was Artistic Director from 1976-1978.

I had an Accident in 1978.

At Lexington.

In Upstate New York.

Alfred Jarry was an avant-garde French playwright, artist, and raconteur, best known for his almost-drawing-style farces, featuring Ubu.

He died in 1907.

Of too much absinthe.

In Paris.

I was, kind of, after my Accident, looking for this autobiography, and I found it at a Used Stuff Sale, maybe my stuff, in upstate New York. It was in a sack along with a loose-leaf, typewritten translation of Jean Anouilh's BECKET. It was in a dark folder, and said JARR across it.

So. Here is his Autobiography, and some of Mine.

Portrait of Alfred Jarry by Pablo Picasso
Used as frontispiece to the 1923 edition of Jarry's *Gestes et opinions du Docteur Faustroll, 'Pataphysicien* (*The Exploits and Opinions of Doctor Faustroll, 'Pataphysician*), sumptuously published by Mary Reynolds and Marcel Duchamp.

Surrealism was not named until over twenty years after Jarry's death. But the Surrealists claimed Jarry as their father, and celebrated his ability to force audiences into discomfort. Freud called this discomfiture *"unheimlich,"* and the Surrealists ran with its liberation of the subconscious through Jarry's introduction of objects and characters simultaneously familiar and foreign.

Definition: 'Pataphysics is the science of
imaginary solutions.

Alfred Jarry
Gestes et Opinions du Docteur Faustroll

I am called Alfred Jarry.

*Note: This is the first line of Alfred Jarry's Posthumous
Autobiography. It comes after a blank, coffee- (one assumes) stained
page.*

I am called Alfred Jarry.

That is, in fact, my name.

Alfred Henri Jarry. Known, to my friends, as Ub.

Merdre.

*Merdre is a word invented by Jarry. It comes from the
French word Merde. I probably don't need to tell you what it means.*

Born 1873, from the magical union of M. and
Mme Jarry, the eighth of September, the day of the Nativity of
the Holy Virgin. In Laval. France, that is, for you people who
don't know.

Of whom there might be quite a bunch, one thinks.

*Or not. I knew when it was, and the 8th of September is a
holy day for those who worship Jarry.*

Currently living on the second and a halfth floor, 7 Rue Cassette, Paris.

In France.

I will tell you some things about me and how I got here.

True or not, it doesn't matter much.

Jarry's "second and a halfth floor" is still there. It's currently in a pretty quiet neighborhood. But it wasn't quiet then.

And apparently Jarry never had much. Writing implements: paper, a supply of ornamental brushes, a bottle of ink. A bottle of Absinthe. A Stone Penis he claimed was a "Reduction" from life.

It was quite Large.

I always loved my mother, Mme Jarry. She was quite beautiful, and somewhat short.

Like me.

Who am short.

She was the offspring of a Judge, and the Heiress of a Major Fortune in the South of France. Also Her Mother and Her Mother's Brother were locked up in Mental Institutions. For a Time.

"Alf," she would say, "Dress Ducal for this." "This" might be the opening of a Store, or a Drinking Establishment. "Ducal" was the best clothes we had.

My father was a carpenter who became a salesman: "Negociant en Tissus." Cloth salesman.

I was six when my mother left my father, M. Anselm Jarry, and took herself, my sister, Charlotte, and me to Saint Brieuc.

"Alf," my mother said, from her throne before her makeup mirror. "I left your father because he was an ass. Truly. An ass."

She sprinkled powder on her lower cheeks and the top part of her breasts.

My father went on supporting his "family," until he died.

I always remember how neatly dressed he was. They were, apparently, a very handsome couple.

And they had me, Alfred.

And before me they had Charlotte.

Eight years before.

Saint Brieuc. A lovely little town. Emphasis on "little." The air was clear and brisk. Cold in the winter. Some snow.

And old people sitting around. Wagons, horse-free, with their connectors thrust up. Horses, standing on one rear leg, the other bent. Trees, always leafless, against the sky. It always seemed to be winter there.

I started to write there. And that's what I am, a writer. Despite . . .

Despite other possibilities, like Drawing.

Or like being Alfred Jarry.

I, too, am a writer. Despite other possibilities.

We moved to Squaw Valley, California, when I was seven. My father, Oakley Hall, after whom I'm named, was a writer. He died in 2008. This was unfortunate, also painful.

I was told I wrote in the style of Victor Hugo.

"Ontogenies," I called them, when I got older. Them being the stories, excerpts, what-have-yous.

In case you're curious: ontogeny is the course of development of an individual organism.

My sister Charlotte was with us. She was already Developing, and I thought of her as my Mother's Sister, usually. And sometimes, not.

Many old people, sitting, wearing Cloth Caps.

In Saint Brieuc.

A lot of old, Classy furniture. All big, and made of wood. My Mother used to say things like: "Ah, the old oak settee . . . ."

She did this sometimes. Talking of Furniture, of Houses, of People as if they were made for her to Look At.

She was, as I learned later, "Curious."

"Curious," in French, is a polite way of saying, "a little Crazy."

And "little" is used in that strange French way of using the diminutive to cover the big: Really Crazy.

I went to school. Bunches of little kids, learning. Becoming like their parents. I did well at school, and went for long walks, up trails, under trees.

My memories of this period are violent.

I had many fights, until I learned to avoid them. I was little, but clever, clever at avoiding pain to myself. I learned very young to go armed. Knives. I have some of them still. My favorite was a sheep-castrator: Beautiful Blade, long and sharp, with a Hook at the end.

To Catch and Hold the Testicle, you see.

Of course you do see.

Alfred Jarry had this split. Small/Large fixed in his head. He was always very handsome, but . . . Small.

And he is best known for writing UBU REX, about a very Large Man, King, Cuckold, Man who wants to become a Slave.

I, Alfred Jarry, Heir of an Heiress, was always intrigued by Slavery. Becoming a Slave. And having Power, Real Power.

This was before I met Ubu, or Hébert.

I was Small. "My little Pou-Pou Enfant," as Mme Jarry called me. I may have been little, but I was Tough. And an Explorer. I explored.

I explored the neighboring houses, their whereabouts, their grounds. The town was not really, as I remember, very big.

I also explored people's reasons for doing things they did.

Uncle Jacques ran a farm, and hired between three and six people a day. There were always the same people. "Red," who was Old and had no red hair that I could see, "Squatty," who was tall and thin, "Mme Death," who was attractive, and there was no Monsieur Death.

And I remember Hating my Father. Absolute Hatred.

Actually, this is traditional. The children of split parents always hate the one who's not there. Or usually. Sometimes, unfortunately, they hate the one they're with.

So Jarry was the child of a "divorce." Or mentally he was, no actual divorce having happened. Jarry's mother was always "Mme Jarry."

We lived on a piece of property that belonged to Mother's Father.

I have a faint memory of trees, standing around like an army after a big battle. And houses, slumped in the center, old.

I went to school each day. I was dressed like a small "man of affairs," a cap, a three-button coat, small corduroy pants. Brown boots. As if I were from another century. I had a leather-covered notebook, too. It just fit in the right-hand pocket of my coat. I would write things I wanted to remember from school in it, and my other writings too.

It is curious to look at now.

All the short examples from the mind of a Gnome. All printed very carefully in India Ink, with drawings here and there. I was always very careful with my own stuff, put it neatly back, in Order.

There are sixty-seven leather notebooks, extending from when I was, I think, five, to the opening night, in Paris, of UBU ROI, 1896.

I like those notebooks.

I also like the fact that I wrote in "imitation" of Victor Hugo.

I have handwriting that is virtually unreadable. Always have had. I shout my orders, when I have something to order.

When I went back to Lexington, then in its fourth year, after the Accident, I would shout things, but it was a little, apparently, unclear what I was shouting. Even to me.

I remember once, being in-tox-i-ca-ted, and shouting at Zobel: "Hey, Zobel, Getcha, getcha."

I was known thereafter as the "getcha getcha" man.

I didn't know what I was saying, when I was in-tox-i-ca-ted.

We never saw my father, M. Anselm Jarry.

He went, according to Mme Jarry, through several major fortunes. He made them, and then lost them. He was a salesman, and then the manager, of a wool factory.

The amount of disinterest Jarry betrays about his Father is indicative. Almost all kids betray some kind of interest, but Jarry has very little.

Other than Hatred.

Charlotte used to remember him, and talk about him. I usually left the room.

Mme Jarry wasn't there. Charlotte and I, usually in my bedroom.

Charlotte would stretch a leg out, and say, "Papa would always . . . ." with that sense of what he would do, whereupon I left.

She was, after all, fifteen or sixteen or seventeen.

And Female. This becomes more and more important to Jarry.

Not so much for their sexuality but because they are "different."

It was then that I learned my independence. My ability to roam, with no possible reason, to show up where I was strangely wanted: Boom! I learned about myself — that I was small, very active, and had some kind of effect on people.

I learned the Difference between the Sexes. Not only were my Mother, and Sister, Female, and therefore Different, there was Mme Death, and Mlle Duh, so called because I never knew who her parents were, and she never spoke, just followed me.

I was already becoming Ubique, and hadn't yet figured out who Ubu was.

But I was developing a sense of Reality.

I had an encounter with Mme Death. Mme Mort. She was older, maybe much older, but she had some Gypsy blood in her, and her age was difficult to tell. I came upon her, and her pail, while I was out exploring behind Uncle Jacques' place. Looking for something, though I never knew what.

Maybe this Encounter.

It is June, and she has her shirt off. This baffles me. I am after all, young, say, eight. She has a skirt down to the ground, but no shirt. She turns to me, as if displaying her breasts. And very handsome they are, too.

I am Dressed for School, with my notebook.

"Ah, M. Jarry," she says in her rumbling voice.

I stand there for a bit. Paralyzed by Pleasure/Pain.

Remembering my Mother's breasts. Big, and Hard on the Ends.

I say: "Pardon me, Mme Death."

"For what, M. Jarry?" She stands with her hands on her hips, thrusting her — Maternities — forward. Big, and Hard on the Ends.

She has put her watering-jug down, and it drips: drip, drip.

"For — ah — hmm." I have suddenly become terrified, at this woman's display of her Womanliness, at her lack of caring whether I see. At her Joy in her Breastly Femininity. At her Maternity, sans child.

It is six or seven in the evening, and late spring. It is warm. Her voice rumbles. She says, "Anh, M. Jarry, you want some wine?"

She stretches, her Upper Body moving.

"Anh," I say. "No, thank you."

I keep looking at her — Maternities. They are Firm and Hard and have Hard Nipples. My Body wants In, and my Mind wants Out.

She tried various things to get me inside, but I essentially bolted, and went home. Where my mother, Mme Jarry, was, in a handsome blouse, covering her — Maternities. And Charlotte, looking respectable.

This encounter with Mme Death made me — well — hard.

I restaged it in many ways, many times, with Me more Dominant.

This may have done something to my thinking. I don't know what, but it might have.

Later I could have dealt with it. With Joy. But then I had trouble thinking.

There is MOTHER UBU.

UBU's Wife.

UBU is usually Lost without her there. She is More Clever, more Ambitious. She insults him – or leads him to a kind of victory.

The usual feeling about Jarry is that he was Gay, or Gay–inclined. He had a tremendous love of Women, but not Sensual Love. If this incident was, as indicated, Jarry's introduction to Sexuality among Women, that is understandable.

Especially with the introduction of his Mother, as an antidote.

I had little Daner. Small, big-breasted. I was, I think, thirteen or fourteen at this point. It was marvelous. She was quite intelligent. She had red hair.

Of course, I am Straight – well, except for one brief period of my life.

We did it in the back of Dana's father's Cadillac. This was exciting.

Jarry couldn't – because he was too young? Or didn't.

I saw Mme Death occasionally, at Uncle Jacques's. She would always smile at me, and move her Body. I smiled back. I looked for her — well, Breasts — but never saw them. They were hidden. I sometimes saw my sister nude, or half-nude. The Breasts were Handsome, but not as Big as Mme Death's, and not as Pointed at the Nipples.

I didn't touch Charlotte's, then. Though I wanted to.

There was also Mlle Duh. I sometimes ordered her to half-strip. But she wouldn't.

This was a brief distraction from my Exploring.

Uh-hunh.

Exploring, I found the Atlantic Ocean. I, however, did not think it was the Atlantic. I thought it was a large lake, with salt water. I was, at this point, relatively Dumb. Bright, but Dumb. You know.

I remember large rocks, and a gravel beach.

That's what it says in my notebook. Which could, of course, be all Lies.

I happened to cross the Atlantic Ocean. I was thirteen, travelling from Europe to Massachusetts. I'd crossed it the other way, earlier.

My father, Oakley Hall, an increasingly well-known writer, in 1958 published WARLOCK. In 1962 the family celebrated its Heading up the Charts, and its being made into a Movie by going – Father, Mother (Barbara), I, my sister Sands, my sister Tracy, and my sister Brett, who wasn't quite one year old – to Europe for a year. In the fall of 1963 they stayed on and put me on a boat in England and then I landed at Philips Academy, a prep school in Andover, Massachusetts.

My basic attitude towards Andover was that it was a good education for people other than me. I was just trying to hang on, get through.

One of the things I did there was to take, outside of School, a secondary Theatre course, run by a student from New York City named Rex. The year before they had performed Jarry's UBU ENCHAINED in a loose translation by Rex, and a short story by Rex, done as a reading.

There were also discussions about Brecht's THREEPENNY OPERA, and how it was based on Gay's THE BEGGAR'S OPERA, and how that was based on THE GRUB-STREET OPERA, or THE WELSH OPERA.

Then we did Brecht.

It was an education in Offbeat Theatre.

In performances we spoke all lines very slowly, as if translating from the German. However, I forget what plays we did.

Already showing my abilities in Doing, and Forgetting.

Which is why this Auto-Biog is a little spotty.

We lived with my Mother's Father, a retired Judge. Actually, we lived in another house close to him. He was tall, and had a huge gray moustache. Large hands. With knobs on them always working, were Grand-père's hands, caressing each other.

In all the years we were there he took me out once. And there we were, Grand-père and Grand-fils — except he didn't like being my Grandfather and introduced me as his "Son." He took me to breakfast at the only breakfast place in town, which I think he also owned. Then we went to church, so it must have been Sunday. Then we went to lunch that his Daughter (my Mother) prepared for him. Then we shook hands and parted.

That was it.

I had a further education in Off-beat Theatre when I was expelled from Andover because they had caught me sneaking away to visit Dana at Bennington College, in Vermont. It's true that this was also after I split open my lip, and head, by diving headfirst into a snowbank that contained a stone bench. This was the first of my diving beauties. The second one was more severe.

After that I went to Los Angeles, with my father, who was working there as a script writer, and attended Hollywood High, and then to the University of California, Irvine. A year early, because I had two 800s on my College Boards.

Hollywood High, despite the stories about it – about a sexy star being found in its food-hall, its location at the heart of the Entertainment Industry – was a kind of sensual nightmare. I remember the Blacks at lunch, dancing, and the highly-organized Jews. And all, at sixteen. Armed. Sexy, volatile, and, at sixteen, Armed.

And Mella, an Egyptian woman, with a beautiful figure and two matching Middle-finger rings.

University of California, Irvine, at its time the newest of the U.C. campuses, had opened the year before. My father was a Teacher of Writing there, and I put myself down as a Theatre Person.

For no reason, other than the desire to know more about it.

So there I was, working on being an Actor, and learning about Theatre. That it wasn't very trustworthy. That you can't go into it and make a niche for yourself and expect to stay there.

That Life is one long audition.

The Drama Department was run by Dean Clayton Garrison. He directed the American Premiere of MARAT/SADE on campus, with a fellow named Robert Cohen playing Marat. I was cast as some nameless psychotic, of which there are a lot in MARAT/SADE.

Dean Garrison liked me and cast me relatively well. Bob Cohen, Instructor of Acting and Professor of Drama, didn't, either one. Although I got into the Repertory Company, which Cohen ran.

This is when I met Bruce Bouchard, and Steve Nisbet and Vano, Michael Van Landingham. Bruce seemed like a kind of demented Surfer. Face smiling. He was always on time, in some place weird. Hair too long, golden blond. What you saw in his acting was his personal Dementia. This made him a good actor. He went to

New York City before the rest of us and made a place for himself there, playing, as I recall, Billy Bibbit in CUCKOO'S NEST, for a long time. We were friends.

Steven Nisbet and I were friends too. He was a good actor, with this quality of Beautiful Loneliness about him.

Vano was studying lighting design at UCI. He was bigger, and lacked a kind of forwardness that Bruce and Steve and I had. But he was cool.

They were all, at Irvine, pretty cool guys.

But this was Irvine. Not the Real World.

I liked Saint Brieuc, but I didn't yet have friends. I wrote constantly. Sometime I wrote pieces of dialogue, other times just notes. And some of them are "shi boooom uh."

You may know what that means, but I don't.

Shi boooom, uh.

Certain friends had started South Coast Repertory, now quite Big, but then fighting to survive. Step One was in a building in Long Beach, and Step Two moved to a venue in Newport Beach. They were all young, and were running the Theatre on basically No Money. So, I began to learn the Beauties of Scavenging in running not-for-profit Theatre.

Scavenging is Theft, without the Legal Problems.

School.

It was the case that I had reached the Secondary Schooling Period and as I was such a good student — without thinking about it — Mother decided we had to go elsewhere so I would get a good education, and become something other than a bum. So we moved about forty kilometers to Rennes.

It was, of course, complex. There I was, Little, with my sister Charlotte, over Twenty, and Mme Jarry, heavily worried about all her Stuff. Which we moved by a huge cart drawn by mules, run by a fellow named Pierre, who was totally deaf.

It was in Rennes that my early writings began to take shape.

Early writing, me.

I began, from nowhere, working on an Elizabethan, even Jacobean play called MIKE FINK. Elizabethan has to do with a five-beat line. A rhythm. Jacobean means that everybody dies in the end. But they also speak in iambic-pentameter. Mostly.

> ONE: 1. A bare stage. Shadows, as of trees at twilight. Enter MIKE FINK, in pathfinder garb, with long Pennsylvania rifle, powder horn, and string of scalps. He takes a chew of tobacco.

> MIKE

I never thought I'd live to see this day.

Wisht I hadn't, come to think on it.

They tell me now the Indian wars is over.

Another god damn treaty writ and signed. Which we got to respect, because we're civilized.

        Ho. Ho. If that's the price o' being
civilized, I'll take the t'other, and the Law
be damned.

*Mike Fink was a keelboat man on the Mississippi River. He
was not only very very Big (estimates vary from seven foot to nine
foot tall), he was also the first person to Pole his Boat from New
Orleans to Pittsburgh (Ohio, not Pennsylvania) with a load of steel.
He was killed at Fort Apache.*

*This play eventually got a Reading at the Public Theatre
under Joseph Papp. I have rewritten it about three hundred times.*

        We arrived in Rennes in our mule-drawn, deaf-man-
driven cart, the day before School started, at about two in the
afternoon. It was a — well — house. I never got used to it. It
had a basement. It was surrounded by other houses, but
looked odder.

        I never knew who owned the house, if we had
purchased it with my Father's money or my Grandfather's, or
what. The important thing was, it had a Basement. Where
UBU got born. Or Re-born.

        *In 1968 I attended the training program attached to the
American Conservatory Theatre. The founder, Bill Ball, arrived
spectacularly in San Francisco, and created one of the best
conservatory theatres in America.*

        We studied Circus Techniques, and Commedia dell'Arte.

        *Bill Ball's office was right off the Green Room, where the
students gathered between classes.*

        *From Bill Ball's Public, but still his, Office, I stole a copy of
UBU ROI.*

And my life was changed.

I didn't know about UBU yet, but something was growing inside me.

Also that summer, at Dana's apartment, I read THE THEATRE AND ITS DOUBLE, by Antonin Artaud.
"Here," I said to myself, "is another kind of Theatre altogether. People Driven to make Theatre. Not happy, not jolly, Driven. Where are these people and how can I become one of them?"

I started school the next day.

Where I met M. Hébert. And the Morin brothers, Charles and Henri.

This is a moment that is very important to Jarry. So, well, note it.

M Hébert was the teacher of a class called Elementary Physics.

I went into his class for the first time. There he was, the focus of all the class. Incredibly large, fat, obese, with a *Caporal*, a triangular moustache. We were all in Uniform: Dark coats, White pants, Boots, you understand. It was Military. I knew what was going on, instantly, and instantly I Looked at the Morin brothers, and Moved to Them.

"Eh," said M. Hébert. "Eh, beh beh . . . ."

He was immense. The size of a pregnant hog. The size of a horse giving birth to twins. The size of a Mountain.

Which I resolved to climb.

From the journals of M. Hébert:

I was there in my class of Introduction to Physics, waiting for some silence, some ordering of the Smells, when Mme Jarry and her little boy, Alfred, entered.

I wear glasses with lenses the thickness of wine-bottle-bottoms, but I still couldn't see them very well. But I could Smell them. O Yes. Rich but Decayed, that was Mme Jarry. Another Smell: Water, Mental Perspiration, a Wariness.

Alfred.

He walked in front. He had a suit on. Old-fashioned, but nice, I smelled.

Mme Jarry was dressed — well — extremely. Extremely well, one could say, except there was that air of high-grade Slut about her. I can't help it, there it is.

I turned and stood, pulled my belly in, smiled.

"Class," I said. "Meet Mme Jarry and her son Alfred, who will be joining us as a student as of today."

Mme Jarry stopped, angled her head, said, "Charmed." Her Smell said she was not "Charmed."

Alfred took a few more steps, looked at me: wide, soft, acute eyes, blinked, and looked at the Class. Said nothing. Smelled, well, more like a Wrestler who has won every match, and then loses the Final due to some strange rule.

"I am Professeur Hébert," I said, extending my hand to Alfred.

He looked up at me. A slight grin hit his mouth, and he said, "Alfred Henri Jarry, Esquire." He looked at my hand for a second, and then extended his, and it was downright Kinglike, his gesture of touching my hand, and then pulling away.

Smelled that way, too.

Mme Jarry said, birdlike, "Well, here is your class of Intro to Physics, Alfred." Turning to me she said, "I hope you can teach him well. He's a little — like my Father, if you understand that."

I Smelled what she meant. I nodded, and smiled, and kept my stomach pulled in, and erased from my imagination thoughts of the Smell of her being spitted and roasted.

"I'll try," I said.

"Another Portrait of Monsieur Ubu,"
sketch for *Ubu Roi* based on Jarry's impression of his teacher M. Hébert, 1896

"M. Hébert, professeur de physique," painted by Jarry while he
was a student at the Rennes Lycée. The beloved science teacher,
nicknamed "Le Père Ébé," inspired Jarry to create 'Pataphysics and
the distinctly unloveable Pa Ubu.

From the collection of Jean Loize, Paris

There we were, all in Uniforms, all paying attention. M. Hébert began the Story of the Rennes Lycée, a truly epic story, one assumed, because M. Hébert spoke curious, haunting prose.

He had a round face with that three-part moustache, *Caporal*. He wore a form of the Uniform of the School, but with strange straps attaching something strange to something else, also strange. He gestured with his hands, and it was like scooping out sections of his midriff, and presenting them to us.

He said at least a paragraph before through his cloud of words, I heard "M Jarry takes . . . ." and so knew that he was talking about me. I stood up and bowed. Even then I knew it was Hébert-ly. EB-ly.

Henri went through a paroxysm of delight, and clapped, and it was all Hébertique or — as it would be a short time later — Ubique.

I smiled at Henri and our friendship was deep and immediate.

The entire class applauded, and M. Hébert stood there with his hands out, as if he had scooped out something applause-worthy.

I knew at that moment that M. Hébert was something. I didn't know What, but Something.

There was an attitude toward M. Hébert. It was probably started by Henri's brother, Charles. Charles was there only briefly. Then he went on pursuing his studies in Paris. He had written, or claimed to have written, LES POLONAIS, the first draft of what became my UBU ROI.

UBU REX, UBU-the-King.

Every time he spoke to M. Hébert, Charles would go into his Eb-stance. His voice would become un-understandable. "M. Ebayert," Charles said, "Whayat the Bum-Fum, do you think?"

M. Hébert nodded slightly and said: "I'll have to think about that one, Charles." And then a combination hand-and-chest gesture, indication we were going somewhere else in his Weird Brain.

It was a fascinating set-up. I mean, to have classes from King Eb, Himself, There.

Hébert became Eb. Ub. Ubu.

A green, beat-up pickup truck roared up Apache Court. Father walked out of the house and shook hands with the man that got out of the vehicle. He was about six-four and slender, and wore a pair of cut-off jeans and no shirt. He was fairly incredible-looking.

Dick Reuter.

I was at that point about Seven. I had no plans for ever being a writer. I was going to be a Lieutenant, in charge of Fighting Men, that I thought of as being armored, surrounding a Castle.

Dick Reuter was Perfect. He took his soft cap off and I noticed he was bald. Then I learned that Dick, called Big Dick (I'm Serious) was over sixty.

He lived across the Road.

He was a logger, cutting, with his twenty-foot chainsaw, redwoods. He was big. He was bald. Also, he was stone deaf. The chainsaw, see, had worked its magic.

He used to get up at 5:00 (I know because I worked for him)
and go up the hill behind his house and kill a deer. For a while it was
a deer a day. A big man, with incredible silence to his movement.
He also talked to himself, gesturing, with his ruined thumb,
past his right ear.
Mike Fink.

Fascinating person, Hébert. Must have all his life been
a failure. He had no ability to teach at all. And no ability, that I
could see, to do anything else. But he did inspire us with a
Dark, Stupid God. An UBU.

One didn't have to search far for thoughts on what
UBU would do next, He was There, Doing it.

To actually have classes from EB, UBU. Wheewoogh.
It must have been a constant lesson in Play-construction.

<u>From the journals of M. Hébert:</u>

I rubbed my hands together, looked at Jarry and the
Morin Brothers, and then looked, not seeing very well, at the
Class of Physics. They were all there: M. Jarry, very short,
very well-dressed. He Smelled — well — less like a Wrestler
today, more like an old man. His face looked different. I saw,
through my glasses, a three-sided moustache on Jarry, even
though it wasn't there.

The Morin brothers, Charles and Henri, were always together. They sat side by side, and they were Mockers. And they Smelled like Mockers. They mocked me. Charles, the elder of the two, had a rustic Smell to him. Henri, the younger, was quite handsome and smelled — well — more Lordly.

And I was there, small, tough, and always asking, well, strange questions.

UBU is a curious creation. But he's mine. The EB people, like Charles, worked with it a little, but it's UBU — Jarry's UBU — who wins the battle.

Of — well — Spectacular Uselessness. And Obscure Menace.

Jarry's UBU is a "Curious Creation."

There are many strange definitions of UBU, based on, say, Jarry's Sense of Size. UBU is Big, Jarry Little. Or based on Jarry's sense of Wit. UBU is Dumb, Jarry Witty. Or Jarry's sense of Neatness. UBU is Sloppy, Jarry very very Neat.

They're fine, these definitions. But they leave out the fact that:

1)   UBU existed, as EB, before Jarry got to school,

and

2)   That M. Hébert was all these things that Jarry gets credit for inventing.

At the same time I was trying to work out Iambic Pentameter speeches for MIKE FINK:

MIKE

O Lord, I humbly think ye fucked me up:

Me, Mike Fink, yer faithful dog.

I'm an old dog, Lord, but I'm a
scrapper.

And I can knock down, drag out, and kick
shit outta any dog on earth.

Even now. So why ye leave me down here?

Chained to nothin, nothin to bite or
bark at, jest howlin, howlin, all the livelong
night.

*I also finished a play called THE OCCULTATION AND
LUMIFICATION OF MR. UBU. This is a strange play, though I'm
not sure there is any way to write about Jarry's life in the theatre
without making it Strange. In the play I made Jarry die because
UBU was alive.*

*This Play works as Theatre, and does not work as Jarry-
biography at all.*

This was the early glimmering of what became an obsession.

Professor Hébert did not know, but Henri had the most
perfect imitation of "Eb."

Now, everyone in the class did a mild imitation of
M. Hébert, but the two Morin Brothers were amazing at it.
Their backs arched, their feet pointed out, and they seemed to
grow bigger, their lower lips got thick, their prose grew un-
understandable.

Henri was the better of the two.

"Eh," said M. Hébert. "Eh, beh beh . . . ."

From that one element UBU began.

Of course, Hébert was not, really, very UBIQUE at all. I think He only wished He was.

M. Hébert proceeded to talk about Physics in his virtually un-understandable prose. I listened, and understood. UBU.

Henri understood too. And Charles, to a certain extent. The class was Physics. M. Hébert didn't explain it too well. I, of course, got a best-in-the-class in it.

Jarry did get best-in-class in Physics. Of course, M. Hébert's Physics class produced no Physicists.

Except, maybe, Alfred Jarry.

Who always did know a great deal about Math — especially in its stranger forms.

The other thing to note is that M. Hébert was reduced to teaching Intro to Physics. He had managed to descend, as a teacher, to a low point. He gave up teaching the year after Jarry left, and took up Politics.

Which he was, Ubiquely, very good at.

"Eh, beh, beh . . . . The odd sing aboot Physics is . . . ." M. Hébert said.

From the journals of M. Hébert:

I thrust my nose toward the class, Smelling, constantly Smelling. My eyes were untrustworthy, my ears, not good, but my Nose! Ah, my Nose.

And I Smelt change in the call. An aura of — well — changeability. From Jarry, mainly. From Henri Morin in a lesser way. Changeability. As if they were planning to imitate someone, maybe.

The whole class imitated M. Hébert, every time he turned his back. Henri had the most carefully observed imitation.

I, too, imitated his posture. Strange, almost Ducklike. And my voice became his. Like a combination of a Duck and an Almost-insane Woman.

"Sso, messieur Jarrry," sang M. Hébert.

"Eh, yess," I sang back.

"Well, ffwhere do yoo come from, and ffwhat are yer plannns?"

"We come from anosser school, not to be mentioned any ffmore. Our pplans are to get ffvery good at Fffysics."

"Ah, ggood. Fyou have coem to the Right Classs, if I may say so."

"Yyes, Sir. Ffthis class has been recommended to us, by the Peripipladinks, Sir."

"Ah, the Peripipladinks," and M. Hébert nodded.

From the journals of M. Hébert:

"Peripipladinks." This word had a good sound to it.
Although I could not remember, right then, what it Meant. I
bent forward, Nose questing. I Smelled Triumph. Curious. I
said the word again:

"Peripipladinks."

I went to the Morin Brothers. "My name is Alfred
Jarry."

"Henri Morin, charmed."

"Charles Morin, ditto," said Charles.

I told them of my admiration of their imitations.

"Go home with us," Henri said. "We have something
to show you."

They showed me their collection of EB texts. I
especially loved LES POLONAIS. I chortled at its perfect
rendering of M. Hébert.

Henri: "Indeed, it's Hébert, all right. My brother
Charles wrote it."

Myself: "EB's a wonderful character. Who plays him?"

Charles: "I do."

Henri: "And I play MOTHER EB."

Myself (disappointed): "Oh. "

I looked at him. I didn't see MOTHER EB, but a
Slender, almost Sexy boy. We were at the Morins' big house,
made of wood, across the street from the Park. We were in
Henri's bedroom.

I suggested myself as Set-creator, Small-parts person, and Director.

There were a fair number of EB texts, not all of them written in the peculiar style I knew as Charles's. Charles seemed to have borrowed EB from someone, as I borrowed UBU from EB.

We started working on the play that afternoon. The characters were puppets, then in a supported-from-below Marionette system. I vowed to do better Heads for them.

And to rewrite:

                    MACTURDY (Henri)

But we have no priest.

                    EB (Charles)

Mother Eb will do the office. Now swear to
kill the King, good and dead.

                    ALL (me)

We Swear.
                              A Beat.

                         EB

Long live Eb!

                        ALL

Hmmmmmmm.

I started my rewriting by adding Hmmmm at the end. A small thing, but writing is a collection of small things, making something larger, and presumably, legible.

EB — and then UBU — was a God, a destructive Maniac. Who tries hard to rule.

He's like a man who has fallen, and forgotten how to rule, but knows that he was, once, King.

I felt like a Lost King in Hébert's class. I was known, if for nothing else, for being absolutely outrageous in my parodies of Hébert, to his face.

It was my only hope.

The thing to bear in mind is that Jarry, in saying, "It was my only hope," in an otherwise jokey reminiscence, is not joking. His Comedy was Crucial to his Existence.

Crucial.

And he is remembered for being in class with M. Hébert. For being wild, thin, small, and asking perverse questions. Like, "M. Hébert, is it the case that the King will talk to the Peripipladinks, or will the Counter-King do?"

I liked the fact that it is MRS. MACBETH who gets MACBETH to go for becoming the King, and so I included that in when I wrote UBU ROI.

MOTHER UBU

After having been King of Aragon, you're content to command fifty churls armed with cabbage-cutters, when you could decorate your chump with the crown of Poland?

UBU

Ah, Mother Ubu, I don't know what you're talking about.

MOTHER UBU

You're so stupid.

UBU

Upon my green candle, King Wenceslas is still alive; even supposing he dies, doesn't he have squads of children?

MOTHER UBU

And who is stopping you from massacring the whole family and taking over?

UBU

Mother Ubu, you insult me deeply. You're going to wind up in the pot.

MOTHER UBU

You poor dolt. If I end up in the pot, who is going to sew up the seat of your pants, I suppose?

UBU

All right. So what? Don't I have buns like everybody else?

MOTHER UBU

If I were you I'd want to put those buns on a
throne. You could get rich. You could eat
chittlins anytime you wanted, and ride in a
carriage through the streets. And you could
have an umbrella of your own and a big
overcoat, down to the ground.

UBU

Ah! The temptation is too great! Buggershins.
Shinsbugger! If I ever meet him in a dark
corner, he'll have a bad quarter of an hour.

MOTHER UBU

Ah, well, old Ubu. Now you're talking like a
real man.

I like it.

It exists.

Merdre.

UBU ROI, UBU REX, was not Jarry's total claim to fame,
and is not. Although it is best known in France, where they all claim
not to know him. If you make a grotesquely large stomach and grunt
several times, they say, "Ah, yes, Jarry," And laugh.

But Ubu was, well, UBU. He had an immense belly, three
teeth, one of stone, one of iron, one of wood, and a single, retractable
ear. Much work had been done on EB by the Morins, and others
before them, but Jarry, with his total and absolute belief, was the key
to making him UBU.

He began to draw UBU as well.

I, myself, had no teachers who mattered in Grade School.
Well, there was Mrs. Dunn, a large woman, very intelligent, from, I
think, Auburn. She was almost gross, there was so much of her. I
remember her reaching, like going after a Child's Toy, into her Dress
for her Bra Strap, and pulling.

We, Charles and Henri Morin and I, did LES
POLONAIS at the Morins' house. It was a Show of Shadows,
that is, Marionettes supported from below, with Lights —
Flames, with Lenses. Charles played EB. We were good, and
got better. I made marionettes of EB, and MOTHER EB, and
MACTURDY. We performed in the Jarry family's basement, or
at the Morins' house, 6 Rue Belair. How strange that I still
remember that address.

Then Charles left to go Paris. Henri played EB. I played
MOTHER EB.

Depending on where the piece was done, the mood
was different. At 6 Rue Belair it was Theatrical. At the Jarry's
underfloor it was a Party. My mother was a Party-giver. And
my sister Charlotte was a Party-goer.

My mother saw the show constantly, and in all its
variations.

Alice Hébert, M. Hébert's daughter, attended
sometimes. I don't know if she even understood that her
father was UBU.

She was, curiously, very good looking.

There was a quality of Glory about her.

She was one of the five children that the Ur-UBU had.

Or his Wife had.

Jarry was getting a reputation. He was a brilliant student, with the kind of focus of a Major Troublemaker. He was short, with bandy legs, and already had the cough of a man who has lived.

And he had – lived.

I, on the other hand, was, while in Grade School, short, with Marine-shaved head, and overweight. I had a pretty tough bunch of friends, Paul Sullivan, Dick Pomin, and John Carnell. They were all Catholics. I was a kind of Protestant. I think. My father was a lapsed Episcopalian, my mother was no longer a Christian Scientist.

I hadn't – lived.

I took every First in the school, knew more about Physics than M. Hébert.

I wore a kind of cape, and had my sheep-castrator sheathed on the side of my left thigh. I wore boots with major heels.

This made me "Bigger." More Height, You understand. I also grew a three-part moustache. Two above the lips, one below. A Caporal.

In imitation of M. Hébert. An Ebism, an Ubuism.

I was at this point rather young, and the three parts were all that grew.

Actually, I have usually had a problem with growing the rest of my beard.

Despite the English "cut-throat razor" given to me later.

By, in fact, Lord Alfred Douglas. Of whom, more. Later.

I used a cut-throat razor. For many years.

At the University of California, Irvine. Where I lived with my parents and sisters in a big old house in Newport Beach. My three-part moustache grew in full and I had a cut-throat razor. It kept getting dull, and I had to search out a whetstone for it. We didn't much have – at least in Newport Beach – the leather strops available for keeping cut-throats sharp.

For those who wonder why MOTHER UBU is the best character in the three shows, they should know that is because I played Her. I looked at Women for their – well – Maternity, and for their oddnesses.

Mme Death was a case in point.

In fact, I had a way of looking at people. I looked at Men for a Conception of Sexuality.

And Women for their Maternity – or lack of – and Controlling Oddnesses.

Which I Had, or could Play, depending.

I felt, and may still feel, that Women work at all times from their Vagina. They are in a way very tight, very controlled. Men are more scattered, as is their Orgasm.

This is not a way I Recommend Playwrights to begin. Well, I don't Disrecommend it either. It's how I began. A sense of Curiosity should hit you right way. There should be no sense of the Actors playing the Parts, just the Parts.

Note, if you will, the way Jarry looks at people: Women – Maternity; Men – Sexuality. And this does not come from Outside, it's basically Organic to Jarry.

Interesting.

I, myself, used my sister, Sands, for Hair. Later I used Dana. And I think I used her well.

But bear in mind that in the two plays I was working on, this is, say, 1971 or '72, one was MIKE FINK, in which Women carry a very small burden. In the other, OCCULTATION AND LUMIFICATION OF MR. UBU, there was only one Woman: Mme Rachilde, the wife of Jarry's Paris Editor.

"Rachilde" played a big part in Jarry's life, but I made her small. Even though, I see now, Mme Rachilde in many ways defined Jarry's life, defined what being a writer was, Jarry's view of the writer's world, and, eventually, of the world altogether.

And Mme Rachilde was an Absintheuse.

I didn't know.

Anything.

Jarry, top, at age 19 (perhaps with his friend Paul Fargue, who later accommodated Jarry by portraying Ubu onstage), in a school photo at Lycée Henri IV, Paris, in 1892 or early 1893

                    EB

I'll be there. But please, accept this little
kazoo.

                   KING

At my age? What would I do with a kazoo? I'll
give it to Buggerlass.

              BUGGERLASS (Mo-Mo)

What a moron.

                    EB

And now I will futz off. (He falls down). Oh!
All help! I've ruptured a gut and bust my
shinsbones!

                   KING

Have you hurt yourself, Eb?

                    EB

I'm dying! What will become of poor Mother Eb?

                   KING

We'll take good care of her, Eb.

                    EB

You are very kind, in your last moment, but
King Wenceslas, you won't be any the less
massacred for that!

"Madame, your character is nothing to shout about, and like all of us you are a negligible assemblage of atoms. But we will grant you one quality: You don't cling."

Alfred Jarry
In a tribute to his patron and champion, "Rachilde"

Born Marguerite Eymery in 1860, and thus Jarry's senior by thirteen years, the gender-bending "Rachilde," whose business card introduced her as a "Man of Letters," was the only widely recognized woman among the writers later called the Decadents. By official dispensation from the prefect of police, she was allowed to venture about Paris dressed in trousers. Today she is recognized as a pioneer of anti-realistic drama. She and Alfred Jarry immediately recognized each other as soulmates. She used her influence to get his UBU ROI produced, and encouraged many other playwrights, actors and directors.

Rachilde and her husband, Alfred Vallette, hosted a salon in the offices of *La Mercure de France*, the journal that Vallette edited and for which Rachilde wrote extensively. Jarry was among their favorites in the constellation of Paris's literary lights. Until Jarry's death in 1907, Rachilde was the most stable influence in his otherwise chaotic life. In 1928 she published a posthumous biography, *Jarry, ou le Surmâle de lettres* ("*Jarry, or The Superman of Literature*").

Rachilde lived to the age of 93. Although impoverished and in failing health, she never stopped writing.

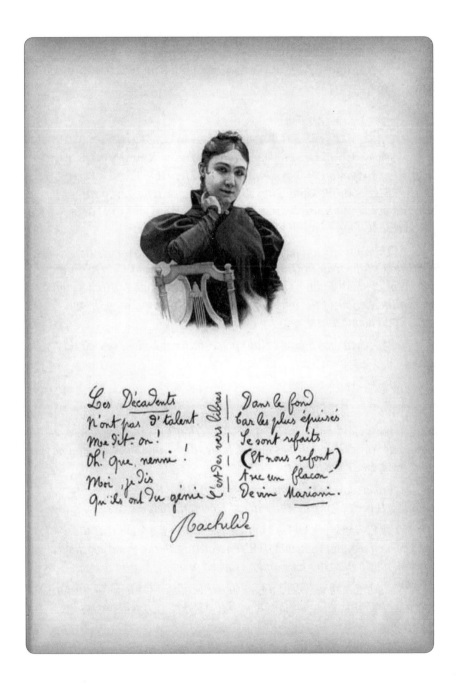

My definition of Plot is fast. Certainly, at times there are pages and pages of thinking, of observing, of word-play; but the Plot moves. The plot may not make much Sense, but it moves Fast.

I was, for non-example, cast in the Irvine Repertory Theatre's production of Brendan Behan's THE HOSTAGE. There were no Blacks in the Company, so I was the one who got to rat my hair and speak in a Caribbean accent. Then I got to star in DARK OF THE MOON, playing WITCH BOY.

Then I went to Boston University to get my MFA — in Writing. On the way I visited New York City. It wasn't a city, but a collection of small towns: German Town, Italian Town, China Town. And in the Center of the whole knot there was Porno Town, from, say, 37th to about 44th.

The City was a fascinating place, but not a place one could relax.

Ever.

Ivan Gold, who ran Boston U's Writer's Grad Program, was from New York City. He was an alcoholic, then, and had written one great book, SICK FRIENDS.

I was working on my first novel, THE ARCHONS, and studying things about the later life of Herman Melville.

"My name is Oakley Hall III," I said to the Vision at the front desk: a woman named MARY, according to the wood-block on her desk, with amazing hair and a crooked grin.

"Ah, Oakley," she said, with her Slightly-Outside of Boston Accent. "I wondered what you looked like." She grinned, crookedly, "Oakley."

One should understand, in my plays, that the Plots are not all Jarryque. A lot of it is Morinique, and Mme-Rachildeique and other-people-ique.

But the truly funny stuff is Jarryque. And this is "funny" in another sense than "make you laugh funny."

Funny in the Gut. Funny in the Real. That kind of Funny.

Also I directed the Plays so that every scene felt like just before, or just after Sex.

Whatever Sex was for Jarry.

If one cares about the Plot, one wants the Character to betray certain things, certain Oddnesses. If one cares about the Plot.

And One (Me) did. UBU ROI has become important in other ways, as a glimpse of something, a forecast of something, as Political or Non-Political, but to me it was a Play that I Wrote — that I Co-wrote — which has a tremendous amount of Activity in it, all of which was based on Plot.

My definition of Plot, not anyone else's. It's not Aristotelian, not Platonic. It's Jarryque.

And Fast.

Around 1974, freshly MFA'd from Boston University, I landed in New York City, penniless. Staying with friends like Bruce Bouchard and his first wife, sleeping in abandoned buildings on First

Avenue. I got this vision of Jarry. Small, slender, wearing an Ubique coat, much too big for Him.

And he stood there, in the erratic lights of the subway stop, at the conjunction of, say, Fifty-Second and First, alone and small, and very powerful. Knowing inside Himself that He would survive.

Of course Jarry had Absinthe, but no matter.

Absinthe.

After I got my MFA I went back to NYC and called Bruce Bouchard. He was amazingly buoyant, and friendly, his blond head moving constantly. He knew tons of people and had stories to tell, O such stories. He had a wife, his first. He met me at some bar or other, and I felt so good about him I requested a place to sleep. Yeah, he said, I could sleep in his apartment.

We drank.

"Can I bring up," da Bouche said, " Your moustache. Uhn."

"It's Jarryque."

"Jarryque?"

"My homage to Alfred Jarry."

"Ah! UBU ROI!" said da Bouche. We offered each other cigarettes. "You'll probably have to shave it to Get Parts."

"Ah well."

Da Bouche already had a Part, and a sequence of Parts before. I was just starting. I felt like Jarry when Jarry got to Paris, arriving in a town that I already knew.

I had my translation of UBU ROI. I had my own plays, MIKE FINK, and the Jarry bio-play. I had a novel that John Cheever had said would be immediately snapped up by a big New York City firm. I felt On Top of the World and Lost, at the same time.

But I still didn't know what it meant to be Jarry.

I didn't understand his Hunger — not for Fame, but for Understanding.

Being Understood.

And I still think he isn't. Understood.

My weapons for the War on New York City all failed.

Even the Novel.

Playing MOTHER UBU was interesting. I never told anyone this, but MOTHER UBU was a combination Mme Jarry and Mme Death.

Not the sexuality of them, but the Control.

Control. Controlling UBU.

UBU is going to do something Weird. MOTHER UBU will then humiliate him. Absolutely. Unless we, the Ubus, are in Public. Then MOTHER UBU praises him. But obliquely.

UBU is basically a Moronic show of Adolescent Attitudes. Can you imagine being Married to that? I couldn't, and so I began to Imagine.

Also in New York City I ran into Michael van Landingham, that Lighting-for-Theatre friend from UCI, and we had this strange idea of setting up a Theatre Company. Where? was the question that obsessed us as we drank in strange clubs, in Bars, Homes.

I got most of MOTHER EB's, MOTHER UBU's thinking later, in Paris, from Marie, the breasty Overblown Hooker. Not to Do It myself, but to Watch, and Understand her Feelings, after Sex, before going out and poisoning herself on Absinthe.

Absinthe.

From Mme Death I received the possibility that all Women are Whores, from Marie the possibility that all Whores are Women.

That was Wrong: some Whores are Men.

Mme Death's is probably Right.

It's Research.

We rehearsed LES POLONAIS like a real Play, moving hither and yon, though we were actually doing it with Puppets.

So we were looking for a Theatre, but in the meantime, I started the Ubique Company to produce, among other things, my translation of UBU REX.

But not using Puppets. Using Actors as Puppets.

We had to learn to move the Puppets. As different Characters. For instance, the motion, the Presence of a Woman, is different. It has to start from a different point in the body: a Man moves from his breast, his groin, his head. A Woman moves from her shoulders, and from the mystery between her legs.

I saw some "Beautiful Women" in Paris, who moved from their Chest, but it's Man-like, oriented toward Men, supposed to "Turn Them On."

I prefer the other, mysterious one. And that's the way I had MOTHER EB's Puppet move, and when I played her, that's the way I moved.

From the motionless point at the bottom of the spine, whence comes all the Wisdom Woman has.

Which is quite a bit.

I started looking for work.

I found it when a fellow named Dr. Harold Goldberger said he needed some help at this Mental Health Clinic, the West Side Center for Mental Health, on 162nd Street, right smack in the middle of Harlem.

Interesting, and a little terrifying. We were, America that is, in the middle of massive Federal Monies for Odd People. And there were some odd ones there. Basically, Women getting psychoanalyzed, and Large Men waiting.

All Black.

I was supposed to be a Guard.

Oh, Sure.

Dr. Goldberger was a middle-sized man, of middle weight, who sensed problems before they came. I guarded the West Side Center for Mental Health for five months, and never got into trouble. Because Harold Goldberger was there.

He drove a Citroen that had Air Suspension, and went something like a foot and a half up and down.

He was not a Psych Doctor, but an M.D.

I rented an apartment on First Avenue and 78th Street, from an old Mafioso who ran a shoe store. It was a very nice apartment, but a six-floor walk-up, and because the City said anything over five floors had to have an elevator, he rented it to me for $25.00 a month. This was cool.

I got on the phone to Plymouth, Massachusetts, and proposed to my friend Meg — Mary — from Boston U. She said okay, if I proposed to her Father first.

Catholic, I guess.

I did, He said, Okay, if I became a Catholic.

I said, uhm — Okay.

Meg said that an old school teacher of hers was now Archbishop in the Catholic Church, there in Plymouth. She gave me his number, and I set it up so that I could get briefed on what the Catholic Church was, and how it did it, in one twenty-four hour session with the Archbishop.

With, as I recall, Wine.

Between my stints at the West Side Center, I went to Meg's house, the most magnificent house in Plymouth, on large grounds at the top of a hill. It looked like something out of Poe, and there was a cupola on top, which I found out was actually haunted, by a Widow who was waiting there for her husband, a man lost at sea and never found. Met the Family: Dr. Gormley, a tribute to doctors all over the world; Mrs. Gormley, a tall woman, regal. The kids, of whom Meg was the oldest, her many sisters (the next one married Richard Meier and I bet he didn't change his Jewish religion); they were all beautiful, and there was one son. I met with the Archbishop for twenty-four hours, became a Catholic, married Meg, beautiful ceremony, settled in on First Avenue, and started directing UBU REX.

I liked Directing. A lot. And the EB plays were exciting to rehearse, as Puppets — to do with/as Puppets — and exciting in terms of Audience Interest.

Or total lack of interest. I didn't care. When we were UBU, we were UBIQUE, and Merdre to the rest of the world.

This is about the first time we get a sense of the real Jarry, the one that stayed with him.

Actually, probably, forever.

Or at least until he Died, and probably after that.

I also liked directing a lot.

Audiences did come, Adults.

Word-of-mouth, basically. All the tall, skinny men, the overweight women. And they howled with laughter. This was a revelation to me, as alleged playwright, how Funny they found it.

I don't think I wrote it to be Funny. That is: Funny — Amusing. I wrote it, I think, as a Violent Dialectic, It should be more Horrible, than Funny.

Ah, Merdre.

Now, be aware, these audiences were accustomed to Puppetry, Puppet-shows.

There has never been any formal criticism of Puppetry. In any case, the people came and laughed, and kept coming. And their laughter did not indicate simply amusement, but understanding.

We did UBU REX with a cast of five. I didn't see how Jarry had done it with a cast of Four, but he has memories of playing Mother Ubu, and one of the Plodins besides. That struck me as Too Tight.

Our theatre was a fabric store on 22nd Street, which we used at night.

I wasn't worried about the Actors, or the Play. I was worried about getting people to see it, in New York City. Where UBU REX

*has been done millions of times, in millions of ways. I had to get
people to understand it, as I saw it.*

And what I saw, basically, was Puppets.

Actually, there was never any formal criticism of
Puppetry until I opened my UBU ROI in Paris, Then they, the
Critics, were critiquing away as if it were a new KING LEAR.

Critiquing, as I say, the Wrong Form.

How could Critics who have never seen Puppets have
any understanding of Good or Bad in Puppetry?

The Audience in Rennes knew puppets. And they
approved. Definitively.

This seemed good, to me.

*I was usually the Director/Translator. Sometime I would
replace whoever could not come. It was never UBU (Richard Zobel).
It was sometimes MOTHER UBU (various). When this happened,
Wendy Chapin, the Stage Manager, would do all the stuff that I did
as Director.*

*Which involved moving Masks and Directing the one
Fresnel (short-shot-light) that we had.*

It worked — well — Fine.

Mo-Mo, who spoke haltingly, as if retarded, which he
was, spoke very clearly, as BUGGERLASS or as the CAPTAIN,
in Rehearsal and in the Shows.

UBU (still EB at this point) was, first of all, BIG.

This is the Element that is usually forgotten by Directors. When He is On Stage he takes up a fair amount of it. Size. Bulk. Immensitude.

The next thing is Vocal. UBU is loud.

So the rest of the Cast (Puppets) is:

1) dealing with UBU as Big, moving around Him, and

2) dealing with UBU as Loud, torqueing their heads away.

The Ubique Company rehearsed UBU REX trying to get a Puppet-quality with Actors who may have never seen puppets in their lives. Steven Patterson was a tall, skinny, good-looking kid who had a remarkable ability to play parts based on Physicality. Patterson was great as MACTURDY and BUGGERLASS. Richard Zobel was perfect as UBU: balding, long-nosed, erect, made-up Obese, with a large mask. I myself, who had seen puppets, was pretty good as BUTTOCKSMOUSTACHE.

We became known, at school, as the "UBU Crowd." Myself, and Henri, Mo-Mo, and a big fellow named Boudin. Boudin was not involved with UBU, at first, I just liked him because he was Big.

I, in my cape and knife, Henri in a sort of extra-real yellow suit, that the censors at the school passed because it was a suit, I guess; Mo-Mo, who dressed the way an idiot would in a terrible, and terribly designed play; and Boudin, who looked Tough.

And I don't think M. Hébert understood the ridicule. Actually, I know he didn't understand the ridicule, although it was relatively hard to miss. When he was facing me, I loved inventing words.

"Physics is Fahrrr," I said. "Sir, you have well-demonstrated the scazoon of peridowing. But what do you think of the Otoeir?"

"Ah," he whuffled. "Good point, Jarry. Let me, ah, think about it."

I basically lectured M. Hébert in an UBIQUE tongue. And of course, M. Hébert "understood" it all.

And so the "language" of the UBU plays evolved. HORNSCAZOONS came from the old version of LES POLONAIS. UPON MY GREEN CANDLE was actually used by Boudin. Curious how if one pays close attention to one's Peasant Surroundings, one can get beauties from it. I paid attention. I paid very good attention.

And one of the things one learns, from paying very good attention to peasants around one, is the almost extra-real quality that Sex has. They don't talk about Sex much, but they are constantly indicating it.

Or that's the way I saw it.

"Merdre" I got from myself — and from Hébert. Once, when his back was turned, I heard him say, "Eh, beh beh . . . Merdre."

Merdre. Sheee-ins. This was my beginning, of translating Jarry.

A making of Shit into Sheeeeeins, just as Jarry made Merde into Merdre.

UBU

Sheee-ins!

MOTHER UBU

Oh, that's nice, old Ubu. You big bum.

UBU

Why I don't bury you, Mother Ubu —

MOTHER UBU

It's not me, old Ubu, it's someone else should be murdered.

UBU

Upon my green candle! I don't know what you're talking about.

MOTHER UBU

Ubu, are you satisfied with your life?

UBU

Upon my green candle; Shins, Madame, of course I'm satisfied. When one is Captain of Dragoons, personal aide to King Wenceslas, decorated with the Order of the Polish red eagle, and retired King of Aragon-- Hornscazoons! What more could one want?

And M. Hébert liked me because I was "Eh, beh beh . . . good at Physics."

This is a curious memory on Jarry's part, since the evidence is that M. Hébert hated Jarry, but was terrified of his seeming (or actual) brilliance. It is also the case that M. Hébert was a major fool, and hung on to his job as professor out of luck.

In 1892 Hébert retires from teaching, and goes into politics, very right-wing, a Catholic, and an anti-Dreyfusard.

And, of course, Hébert was pretty good at it.

This, too, is somehow classic Jarry. Ubique.

I was good at making puppets and got better at it. They were supported from Below. This gave us an actual Stage. The amount of memory involved in figuring out Who's saying What to Whom, and while having to manipulate, say, MOTHER UBU while making sure MACTURDY is about to enter. With only two hands. The effort to know Who's doing What to Whom, was quite tremendous. Henri was very good at it.

Working on the UBU plays made me realize what the Director has to do with the making of a play. I Directed, and thought about what EB/UBU had been doing, what the PLODINS were Doing, before they came on Stage. What the Dream-Life of each Character is, and how it Affects his Movement. I thought about all this stuff, and Directed pretty well.

And Henri was good at taking Direction.

"You know," I'd say. "Ub's not in control, but in His mind, He is. Why don't you make Him stand a little — um — Straighter?"

"All right." And Henri would make his Puppet UB stand in that UBIQUE way, Hips forward, Spine resting.

So there was UBU, huge, standing in the UBUesque way. MOTHER UBU, skinnier, standing with her body forward. This is all Puppets, bear in mind.

And on the set, I built a Bed. To indicate what UBU and MOTHER UBU did. Or did not do.

Merdre.

Zobel, as UBU, was dressed in a rough, almost-white coat with a tremendous amount of padding. MOTHER UBU needed to be a lot Taller. We tried this at first by putting a Fake Head over the actor's head, and later resorted to very High Shoes.

I put in a fair amount of time on Silence. The Silent, body-directed response to UBU's presence. The elements of Fear, Discipline, and Abject Love (on the Part of the PLODINS). The elements of Discipline, and Abject Despisal (on the Part of MOTHER UBU)

It is, after all, She who sets up the Plot. This is borrowed from MACBETH, and works fine in both Plays. What it means, other than a MOTHER-UBIQUE understanding of Lady Macbeth, is that MOTHER UBU understands a Good Deal about the workings of the Government. This makes most of her dim-lady responses to UBU fake.

SOLDIER

Mr. Ubu, you dropped your earhole-scissors.

UBU

I'mena kill you with my shinshook and my face-chopper.

MOTHER UBU

How beautiful he is with his helmet and armor.
He looks like an armored pumpkin.

UBU

Ah. Now I'm going to mount my horse.
Gentleman, bring on my phynancial horse.

MOTHER UBU

Ubu, your horse won't be able to carry you. He
hasn't had a thing to eat in five days, and
might as well be dead.

UBU

Well, that's fine. I pay out twelve cents a
day for that nag, and it won't carry me? Ubu's
Horn! Are you teasing me? Or robbing me?

> *MOTHER UBU blushes and
> lowers her eyes.*

UBU

All right. Bring me another animal, I won't go
on foot, horngutsack!

> *An enormous Horse is
> brought in.*

UBU

I'm going to get on top of it. Better sit
down, or I'll fall. *(The Horse goes.)* Ah! Stop
this animal! Great God! I'm going to fall and
be dead!

MOTHER UBU

What an imbecile. He's up again. Ah! He fell
off.

UBU

Body horns, I'm partly dead. All the same, I'm
going to war, and I'm going to kill everybody.
Woe to him that don't march straight. I'll
stick 'im in my pocket, with wrenching of the
nose and teeth and ex-traction of the tongue!

MOTHER UBU

Good luck, old, Ubu.

UBU

I forgot to tell you that you will be regent
in my absence. But I have the account book,
and it's too bad for you if you rob me. I
leave you the Plodin Lap-Bone. Farewell,
Mother Ubu!

MOTHER UBU

Farewell, old Ubu! Kill the Czar good!

*Fanfares. The ARMY moves
off.*

```
          MOTHER UBU (alone)

Now that yonder obese burlesque is gone, we'll
try to do some business, murder Buggerlass,
and get possession of the treasure.
```


At first we worked in my apartment. Zobel had a Pittsburgh accent for his UBU. One of our MOTHER UBUs was British, but sounded Jewish. The THREE PLODINS were – well – Adaptable.

But when we moved to the Performance Space, the acoustics were much different. We worked then on Character Stance: getting to a position that's Ubique, Mother Ubique, Buggerlassesque, etc.

And Comic Hold-Moments. Get to a point where the Bodies are Weird-Beautiful, and Hold. The variation in Hold-Moments: Hold for One, or Three, or occasionally, Five beats.

For this purpose I made our first Prop: a Pair of Scissors, about four feet long, painted Black. They open and shut, and have Teeth in them.

UBU's Hold-moment Prop.

I still have those scissors. After the Accident and through the tremendous amount of moving around the Country that I did afterwards, they still hang on the front wall of my writing studio.

There is a way, once the sense of the Play has been worked out, of making a series of still-photographs of the Show. Virtually every scene, and there are a lot of them in UBU REX, features a Hold-Moment, a Process-Shot, Moment of Ubique Reality.


```
               UBU

Bring on more nobles. Since I'm planning to be
rich, I'll have them all executed and take
```

over the vacant properties. Go on, stick all
the nobles in the hole. (NOBLES are piled in
the Trap.) Hurry! Faster! I want to make some
laws now.

OTHERS

This should be good.

UBU

First I'm going to reform Justice, and then
we'll get to Phynance.

JUDGES

We are opposed to any changes.

UBU

Sheeeins. First, Judges will no longer be
paid.

JUDGES

How will we live? We are poor men!

UBU

You may have the fines you levy, and the
properties of anyone you condemn to death.

FIRST JUDGE

Horrors!

SECOND JUDGE

Infamy!

THIRD JUDGE

Scandalous!

FOURTH JUDGE

Absurd!

Hold-Moment.

ALL JUDGES

We refuse to judge under such conditions.

UBU

Judges into the hole.

This Hold-moment worked.

We opened the show in the fabric store in Manhattan. The fabric-designers and sales-people and friends of our actors came to UBU REX. And laughed a lot.

I'm still not sure they laughed for the right reasons, but they laughed.

Puppets on Stage.

It worked.

And all this time Vano and I were meeting in bars and talking about creating a theatre. We needed a Place.

Henri was good at a lot of things. And UBU was one of them. UBU has always represented to me: Life, of a sort. Yes, UBU was dumb. But He enjoyed Life. And wore a Mask.

He had no personality, only a good Mask.

NOTE: Masks. Even today I get asked: Why Masks?

Masks were the original form of theatre. In both Greece and the Orient, Masks kill any facial beauty or ugliness, and make you Blank.

Or the Character.

Morin and I used them to play hard Characters: Crooks, Thieves, Cardinals. They made me, as a shy boy, open. They loosened me, I think, because there was a Mask, and I played That.

Very Heavy Makeup has the same effect. You aren't You, Playing a Part — You Are The Part.

The Dionysiacs used wine lees to Make themselves Up, and the Old Romans made a Mask of the Dead One, to be worn by a Living One. Masks are Other. You put Them on, and You are the Character.

There.

Our audiences: Of course my Mother, She was supportive. As was Henri's. And Mo-Mo was there, either as an Actor or as a Moronic Audience Member. And we began to pull others, tall gaunt men, small, overweight, cloth-headed women. And they Laughed. Hard.

Ma Ubu and Ubu in UBU REX, directed by the author and performed by The Firlefanz Puppets at Steamer No. 10 Theatre, Albany, New York, in January of 2010

Puppeteer, upper left: Meave Tooher

Photos above and at right by Tom Taylor

Ubu nods off while Buttocksmoustache and Bar-Snister, having slain the bear, plot their escape.

Puppeteers: Ed Atkeson, Meave Tooher (bear), Monica Miller, and Paul Jossman

FIRLEFANZ PUPPETS PRESENTS

Oakley Hall III's

UBU REX

BY ALFRED JARRY

MUSIC BY MARY JANE LEACH

Jan 8 & 9 at 8pm, Jan 10 at 3, 2010
at Steamer No. 10 Theatre
500 Western Ave, Albany NY
518-438-5503 · www.steamer10theatre.org

Above: Ma Ubu and Ubu, with puppeteer Ed Atkeson at right.
Left: Poster designed by Ed Atkeson

Photos by Tom Taylor

You may notice that Jarry repeats himself at times. This may have to do with his absinthe-riddled Brain at the time he was Writing this.

You may notice that my own story skips about a bit and repeats itself as well. There is a different problem with my Brain.

And the nature of people laughing hysterically doesn't matter very much. Doesn't matter –

At All.

'Pataphysics. Epi meta ta physica. It was a concept and all mine: Beyond Metaphysics. Beyond beyond physics.

'Pataphysics is as far beyond Metaphysics as Metaphysics is beyond Physics. If you can understand that.

And trust me, a lot of people don't. It is, in fact, Surreal.

And Jarry is dead before Surrealism arrives.

We began to rehearse UBU CUCKOLDED. This has two fascinating new characters in it. One is ACHRAS, who spends most of the play impaled, and one is UBU's CONSCIENCE.

And strangely enough, CONSCIENCE was relatively hard to write.

I think of CONSCIENCE as "It."

"It" has both Sexes.

I also thought of it as Unmasked.

You would need the Sexual Equipment of both Male and Female to do it. I know such people exist, but they are probably not drawn towards the Stage.

As we know it.

I remember a scene from UBU CUCKOLDED with pleasure:

```
                    Scene: ACHRAS
                    (impaled)


                    UBU

By my green candle, my sweet child, we will be
happy in this house!


                    MOTHER UBU

Only one thing is lacking for my happiness: to
see the respectable host who has given us all
this.


                    UBU

Don't worry: foreseeing your wish, I have put
him in a place of honor

                    UBU shows the Stake.
                    Shrieks and a Nervous
                    Crisis by MOTHER UBU.
```

My Mother took tickets. We had lots of Titles: UBU ROI, LES POLONAIS, EB TRAPPED, EB AND THE POLACKS. Actually it occurs to me we had more titles than shows. For example, LES POLONAIS and EB AND THE POLACKS were the same show. Roughly.

I say Roughly because we almost never referred to the script. We had set-ups for jokes, and the audience response would dictate the way the joke would go. Set up, get Bigger, Poom: Joke.

That's why it's all short scenes.

Yep, it's a Five Act Drama that can be done in Twenty Minutes. Pretty good, Mr. Jarry. Pretty good, Mr. Ubu, Pretty good, Mr. Morin. Pretty good, Mo-Mo.

Zobel created an UBU mask that was very much based on Jarry's UBU. Which I suspect Zobel had never seen.

It was Big, and Pyramidal, and had a hole where the mouth was. Which developed a corner that was smudged with cigarette smoke, because we walked around Southern Manhattan to raise walk-ins for the show, which ran for two weeks. As I recall, Ubu and two or three of the Plodins walked around. The others couldn't make it, for some reason.

Like Work.

I did other things too. It was, after all, the period when people, especially men, learn things, and do them here and there. I was in Rennes for three years, 1888-1891, fifteenth through eighteenth year of My Life, so called.

I was, as they say, in my prime, hitting on all eight cylinders, as they say now. My sister Charlotte had grown quite Breasty, and I used to touch Them, occasionally. They were fun to touch, but never developed the Hard Extensions of Mme Death's. I saw my mother's Breasts occasionally. They were more exciting, to me.

But not like Mme Death's. Oh no.

Mlle Duh developed, and developed a name, which I have forgotten.

And I fooled around with boys sometimes too, Henry, and Mo-Mo. Mo-Mo was stupid, but very well-hung.

In Rennes we, the Jarrys, led relatively unobserved lives. It is there that I am supposed to have said, when asked where I spent each night: "In the brothels." And they felt this might be true, because of my Voice and my General Attitude.

It was not True. I am not even sure where the Brothels are, in Rennes.

In Paris, I know where they are.

In New York I soon discovered where the best Bars were. There were some good ones here and there, but the best ones were the Gay Bars, especially on the Lower West Side. Actually I preferred the Female Gay Bars. Loud Music, beautifully chosen, Women in all Forms, only occasional Fights.

And they, the Women, would buy for me, too.

I don't know why. I didn't look like a Lesbian about to Happen.

In Paris I left my card with Marie, and it was Watching, not Doing.

And Drawing it.

In Rennes, I found a pile of old books, treating all Sexuality from a Medical Point of View. Very strange stuff, too. Probably made me rather strange in my responses to Sex, and may still.

Yep.

We continued to rehearse UBU CUCKOLDED. It was rather like the big leagues — where I eventually wound up, in Paris, at the Theatre de l'Oeuvre — having our rehearsals. We had certain times we had to arrive at certain places. We'd started out, just Charles and Henri and I, out behind the Morins' house in the lumber-loaded, old-farm-smelling building. Then Charles left and we had Mo-Mo. Then we moved to the Jarry family's basement. We had Blacks (black cloths, hanging), and Shelled Illumination, and the Acoustics were pretty good.

And our Lights were amazing.

Lights.

Kate Kelly, a girl who was beautiful, and Irish, told us she'd heard that a Theatre Complex in Lexington, New York, was looking for a Theatre Company.

I spoke to Evelyn Weisberg, who ran the place, and we went up and looked at it. The place was filled with Garbage. Not only hundreds of bags of household junk, but wagon-wheels, mattresses bleeding horsehair, old sewing-machines, broken stage sets. And many of the garbage bags were broken open.

This made me a little despondent. The place had not been run as a Theatre Company in some time, and, when it had been, it was a Theatre Camp for Little Kids. Arrgh.

Then I looked up, in the Barn Theatre, and saw Lights, literally dozens of Lekos and Fresnels (long-shot, and short-shot lights). All hung very carefully, aimed at Nothing.

Lights!

I was sold.

The author in 2010, directing UBU REX, performed by The Firlefanz Puppets at Steamer No. 10 Theatre in Albany, New York

Photo by Luanne Ferris, Albany Times Union

And the Gas to run the Lights belonged to the City of
Rennes. Ah Theft. Wonderful theft.

There's probably not a Theatre in the world that
doesn't have some Kleptomaniacs on its staff.

*I was at this point semi-happily, newly, Catholically
married.*

*We lived at 400 E. 78th Street. Six floors up. The apartment
had enough room for two, Meg and me. My study was in the corner
of the living room. Made from all my books on scabby shelves. A
desk, a typewriter, access to coffee.*

Meg, Big hair, ready, crooked grin.

Though I remember her mouth had a funny twist to it.

*I didn't violate my Oath until after the Accident. This
didn't prevent me from having thoughts.*

Most of the Ur-UBU texts didn't even contain
MOTHER UBU, so in a sense She is an Invention of Mine. And
she's pretty good, mainly because I played Her, with my two-
tone voice, and my racking cough.

Besides, we didn't use women. For one thing, we
didn't know any.

*Thoughts: Kate I had slept with before my marriage, and I
knew her warm, loving, red-headed approach.*

Now that I know some women, I see this might have
been short-sightedness on our part.

*More thoughts: Gretchen Van Ryper. Forbesy Russell.
Forbesy was a definite female beauty, and volunteered to play the
Bride of Frankenstein's Monster in my play, FRANKENSTEIN. She
lay there for an hour to come to life, nude, for about Two Seconds.*

Now that I know Mme Rachilde. Now that I
remember, and vividly, Mme Death. Now that I have watched
Marie go from first-class hotel room to the Rat Mort, a Lesbic
Bar. Now that I have seen the men, short, long, tough, pay for
it, yet I know Marie as a full-tilt Lesbian. Do the men know
what their money pays for? Do they care?

There were others. Sofia Landon. Winship Cook.

*1977. New York City. Winter. An all-Female production of
Beckett's WAITING FOR GODOT, with Winship Cook, a very
sensible actress, whom I loved because of her ability to "puppetize"
anything, playing the character of LUCKY.*

*Winship was LUCKY in some interior sense. Her Silence,
for most of the show, was a test of Presence.*

*I had at this point Artistic Directed for a year. But I had
never seen Winship looking — well — Attractive before.*

*She played from the point of view of Sex. Just before, or just
after.*

This was a curious kind of Learning Experience.

Sex, just before or just after, struck me as a great place to work characters from.

Whatever that was to me — it was probably not the same for Jarry.

In a sense I was lucky that I didn't sleep. But if I had, I'd have dreamt of Women. Masked, and Nude.

So there we were, a short Genius (me), a great Actor (Henri), and Mo-Mo, who would be a total idiot offstage, but on Stage, in a mask, his voice was MACTURDY's.

But with UBU CUCKOLDED we had some problems. Not enough Cast. So we went looking for actors. Boudin, from school, was cast as UBU's CONSCIENCE. That worked fine until opening night, when he forgot all his lines and beat the crap out of UBU.

This charmed our audience. They had never seen such real Violence on stage before. Well, it was one Puppeteer beating the crap out of another Puppeteer. It seemed real.

Actually, it Was real.

I was accused of taking Jarry and making him Harder. The Directors I spoke to said that Jarry is great for Actors, because he made them be, well, Puppet-like. My feeling was that Puppets was what Jarry understood; he did not understand Actors. He would have been right at home in the era when Actors played Characters, Types: EVERYMAN, or THE DEVIL, or PUNCHINELLO. He writes:

>*The actor should use a mask to envelop his*
>
>*head, thus replacing it with the effigy of the*

CHARACTER. The mask should not follow the masks of the Greek theatre to indicate tears and laughter, but should indicate the nature of the Character: the Miser, the Waverer, the Covetous Man amassing crimes . . .

Jarry understood the Masks Breaking Down, Revealing.

This was true in America, too. Masks broke down and revealed the total insanity that builds Theatre, and that grows from it.

The characters in Jarry's Plays, Surreal though they are seem Real. Have Real Wants, Real Fears.

We were all, that's Me, Zobel, Patterson, Rotblatt, Winship Cook, at a sensual period in our lives. At that point, Winship was the only woman among us. It was bizarre. And interesting.

She usually wore coveralls, and had an amazing ability with accents. Long haired, sleepy-eyed, she was the first to laugh at my/Jarry's attempts at Comedy.

I was using MOTHER UBU as the focus of all sexuality in the Actors. I had to reroute the Sexuality we all felt for Winship through the Male Actor, but female in intent, of MOTHER UBU.

It was Sexy.

Curious: we never performed UBU ROI for Professor Hébert, though I wanted to. We just didn't.

I suppose I hadn't got my Shock-'Em Hat on yet.

It became fairly notorious. EB, as done by Morin and Jarry.

We became fairly notorious too. UBU, as done by Zobel and Hall. Especially when we moved up to Lexington, and began doing anything we could to get attention paid to the Theatre. We were highly portable, having only to take Masks and one Fresnel-light. So we became "Intro to LCT," appearing at civic functions in the nearby town of Hunter, especially the ones, Rotary, Elks, Toastmasters, that happened before 7 AM in the morning.

This altered UBU somewhat. Made him more nasty. Made him screw up the order of the masks.

And people loved UBU REX.

Especially after my Accident, when they couldn't get it anymore.

Sunday. Had to meet my Mother for breakfast, and so I dressed for Eb (School), with a few extras thrown in. A Beret, and Large Forefinger Ring, A Sneer. And went.

It's curious when your Mother has to make dates with you, but that's the way we lived. I walked into La Barberose, and saw her sitting, with coffee already delivered.

"Ah, l'Ecrivain," she said. "Sit, please."

I sat. I was sixteen. This was — well — a little much.

My Mother poured coffee into a cup and handed it to me. "Black," she said.

"Black."

"At this meeting," she said, her Face noble, her Hair perfect, "We are discussing your future."

"Ah," I said, not having too much else to say.

"We were thinking of going to Paris, to get you into a good school."

I shrugged.

"Do you want that? Now, bear in mind, it's Paris." She took a bite from something I didn't have, and a sip of coffee, little finger extended.

I bore in mind that it was Paris and said, "Yes." I could have said, "Oh, yes," to fit the mood better, but I didn't.

And I did want to become a Doctor of Research.

Then.

"All right," she announced, "We're going, When your school year here is over."

Her face closed. The "meeting" was over.

I thought: Farewell to Alfred Jarry Show. This might be Good.

We ran UBU REX in New York City for a couple of weeks. It worked fine.

Then we closed it. And I went up to Lexington.

We met: Henri (UBU), Mo-Mo (MACTURDY and BUGGERLASS), and Jarry (MOTHER UBU).

I signaled for Silence, and began to roll myself a cigarette, from the American Drug, Tabac. I lit it, and said, out of the side of my mouth: "Well, it appears that Jarry has to go to Paris to continue his studies."

Henri ejaculated: "What?" and Mo-Mo began, slowly and largely, to cry.

"What did you say?" said Henri.

"Jarry, with his Maman, must go to Paris. To continue his studies to become a Doctor of Research. This is not a big problem, and there is no use bursting into tears." I looked at Mo-Mo, and he looked at me, so very sad.

I was somehow satisfied that it hurt him so, the fact that I was leaving.

"And so we must set up, " I went on, "A Farewell to Alfred Jarry show."

I looked from Henri to Mo-Mo, who, with tears sparkling on his face, nodded.

We'd decided to run the company between Vano and me. He'd Executive Direct and I would Artistic Direct. Which meant putting together the season, fixing up the grounds, looking for interested people. It was my job to make sure the sets were built and lights hung for each show. I did a lot of it myself.

I spent most of that winter, the winter after I got married, up there cleaning out the garbage from the Barn Theater, and also cleaning garbage out of what would become the River Theatre. I had, as I recall, help from Michael Hume.

Lexington is about three hours north of New York City. I had a couple of hundred dollars saved, and Michael Van Landingham might have had the same. We told the Actors what we had and they agreed to come anyway.

We named the theatre: Lexington Conservatory Theatre. Although at that point there was no conservatory. But we thought there might be. Someday.

We had virtually nothing. No money, no food.

We had some Actors. By luck, and knowledge.

It was On Faith, Lexington Conservatory Theatre, and On Pressure.

Mme Jarry was fairly worked up on the subject of the Farewell Show.

"Alf." She spoke beautifully past carmined lips and perfect teeth. "Can I ask a question?"

I sat there, small, perfectly dressed, ready for School. I said, "If you want to, you can, Maman."

"Then tell me." She hesitated and put a napkin to her mouth as if to pull elements of bread therefrom, though there weren't any. "What are you doing with THE POLACKS? What is this 'Farewell to Alfred Jarry Show'?"

"Well, I am going."

"Well, you're right about that, but are they going to miss you?"

"Oh, I think so."

"Hm." She eyed her food, as if looking for something. Shook her head. "Well, all right. Shall I be there?"

She had never missed one of the UBU shows, but she was asking my permission, so I said, "Oh, yes, Maman, you are invited." I paused a moment and than said: "And dress Ducal."

"Oh, all right." She smiled.

I never said that one of my inspirations for doing the UBU shows was my Mother.

There.

I wish I could say something like this, but I can't.

I can say that my feelings about Fatherhood (My Own) were much impacted by writing and directing FRANKENSTEIN.

About Not being a Good Father, which Frankenstein isn't.

About Fathering a Theatre Company, which I did, and watching it grow, go Berserk, be nice.

About being father to a show, FRANKENSTEIN: I wrote the Script, designed and built the Set, mostly-designed the Costumes, designed Everything, so it would be my Hallucination.

I had some of the American drug, Tabac, which I rolled up in fragments of old newspaper, and we, Henri and I, shared it.

Then we went to class.

And there was M. Hébert. The fact that he had been transformed into EB-UBU didn't transform his monumental Lack of Style. He had none, or rather, he had one: UBIQUE.

He entered class, late, as always, and did his "Beh — eh, eh," opening.

He did the same thing each day: "Beh — eh, eh" and than had nothing to say.

But today: "Beh — eh, eh," M. Herbert said. "It has come to our attention that we are seeing the last of M. Jarry."

A long silence, and then he looked at me. I said, "Ah, yes."

"Aha. And where are you going, one asks?"

"Paris."

"Aha! Well best of . . . We were in Paris once and . . . ."

And Hébert was off. He talked for something like thirty-five minutes on the subject of M. Hébert's visit to Paris.

In the end I responded with something like, "How fascinating."

Which it wasn't.

My mother started serving Deliciosos at six that night. The show, UBU AND THE POLACKS, didn't start until eight. We mingled with the audience. Me, Henri, and Mo-Mo. It was the "Farewell to Jarry" night, so I got a fair amount of attention.

We moved Downstairs. We got ready to start the Show.

"Merdre," said Ubu (Henri).

And we were rolling. We took a break after every Act, and there are Five.

And finally Henri said: "Here's to Poland, for without Poland there would be no Polacks!"

Look at Each Other. Look at the Audience. Blackout.

Lights Up. Bows.

Goodbye.

Lexington was small. Maybe even, Really Small. I once estimated that two people lived in it all year, then revised that to one, because the bartender at the Hotel, a big bearded Russian, actually lived outside of town. Evelyn Weisberg, our landlady, lived there for about five months out of the year.

You got to Lexington by going through Hunter, or through Woodstock, or through Wyndham. From Hunter and Wyndham you made a turn by a hotel — where there was a bar, and that Russian bartender — crossed a bridge (important, later, that Bridge) and there you were. On the right was the Lexington Hotel, grand, beautiful, old-fashioned. It had not seen action in decades. Its beautiful cornices needed paint, the interior needed People. Facing the road was a wide

Reception area, in the back, kitchens, above, two floors with small rooms.

As I recall, the entire Lexington Company used One Shower, located on the second floor of the Hotel.

Not enough showers. Which didn't worry me very much, or at all.

So in 1891 I moved to Paris with my Mother and my sister, Charlotte.

Here is a moment, and a beautiful one. Jarry, the short, machine-voiced Playwright, moves from Rennes to Paris. To Pursue his Studies.

In Ubique terms, maybe. But one has to see other things going on. Ubu was important to him in Rennes, and became more important to him, later. 'Til it took over his life. Yet here we see a good, studious young man, going to his studies at the Henri IV, a real live college-preparatory school, where he studied with Bergson and got very good marks.

But then, and possibly for the first time in his life, he failed. He went to Henry IV for four years − or At least signed up for four − but he never got into any University, anywhere. This is possibly due to his appearance: three-part moustache, hair-growing, etc. but it may have been this failure that set up a whole life of failure.

Of course he is already half-way through his life at this point, but he didn't know that.

Failure, in the Theatre, is kind of expected and after the brouhaha that came around the opening of UBU ROI in Paris in 1896 perhaps seen as inevitable. But Jarry pursued failure, with his graceful form and machine-gun speech. It is as if he expected it for himself, and gloried in it.

We still don't know, or at least I don't, if He Failed on Purpose, or Didn't.

11 Rue Cujas. The address of our first Parisian Abode.

I was struck by the way Parisians dealt with their problems, like a bowl of water from washing the face. Hurl it into the street, shouting, if one is polite, "Gardez-loup!"

If one isn't polite, without.

Chamberpots are similar, but the smell is more intense.

In fact, I was struck by the difference in smells. In a village, or even a small town, the people care about things: like cart-pulling horse turds, they sweep it onto a little angle-board. In Paris they don't. There are a lot more human smells. There is the smell of rot, of fishes, of children.

There is the almost Ubique smell of people: Sweaty. Unbathed.

The Ubique visions: Large Men with their Hands Raised; Tall Women nodding with Concealed Contempt.

And very Odd Slang: words for things that don't have words to describe them. Pee-pee for Pisser, for example.

The night-borne Sounds of Violence in speech, the Rhythm in Beatings, the Rhythm of Breaths in Other Forms.

I loved it.

I arrived in Lexington, this is January, and was basically alone. Meg was in NYC, working on Psychology Today, *and I was in Lexington, trying to make Theatre happen there.*

*I spent from January until June cleaning the two theatres,
installing reworked theatre seats, testing and checking things: there
was a lighting system in the Barn Theatre, and it was pretty good,
there was a sixteen-track input tape player, but no sound system to
run it through. There were no dressing rooms, that I could see. I
built some. There was no ticket-vending place, so I built one.*

*I lived in one of the small houses hooked up to the abandoned
Hotel on the Lexington property. They were small, and there was no
heat, so they were cold. Cold. And it was cold up there in Lexington.
Very cold.*

*There was a girl there, on the property. Judy Martin. She
had a son maybe three years old. Apparently she was the result of
some previous Evelyn Weisberg Theory about Life in the Mountains,
and she and her son were living there, free, in exchange for
supervising the property. She was a Composer.*

*She had a tape of her most recent Composition. It was a 40
input tape. There was all kinds of music on that tape, all hers, from
Beautiful music that sounded very Sixteenth Century, to stuff that
sounded very Negative and Twenty-Second Century.*

*I listened. And began thinking about a play based on Mary
Shelley's FRANKENSTEIN.*

> ONE: 1: WALTON's
> ship, in northern
> seas. (Note: Set
> should be highly
> mobile; it changes
> relatively fast.)
> WALTON there.

CREATURE (voice-over)

Did I request thee, Maker, from my clay
To mould me man? Did I solicit thee
From darkness to promote me?

                    WALTON crosses down
                    to his cabin, and
                    begins to write.

              WALTON (V.O.)

My Dear Sister.

    We have now reached an extreme Northern
latitude, and are forced to make our way very
carefully through the ice, which might crack
us like an egg at any moment. Margaret, I am
more and more convinced that inside the Polar
Circle lies the Land of Eternal Light, the
Eden from which Adam was expelled, as the Holy
Scriptures tell us. Northern Mariners have
told me of the ice-free sea, but none of those
old salts was scientifically equipped as I am.
Ha, does it not seem insanely presumptuous to
be mounting a scientific expedition into
paradise?

    My hair was still short, though I had grown my
Caporal, my three-extension moustache.

    Others thought of it as Military, but I thought of it as
Ubique.

    It was, in fact, Ubique.

    *The strange thing is, despite the Stories of Drinking Binges
in NYC before this, it was at Lexington, that first spring, that I
really started to drink. There was no heat, and it was cold. Cold like
ten below zero, Fahrenheit, during the day. At night, who knows?*

And the other thing was I got to charge my drinking against when the rest of the Company, presumably with some Money, came. Huh, huh.

So I Drank. Sometimes it was Judy and me, but always me.

I wrote in the mornings, and after that cleaned out the theatre, and drank the night away at the bar across the River.

I met a lot of people there and told them all that I was cleaning the Theatres and we were starting a Theatre Company.

They doubted I could do it.

As did I. But I kept on, writing in the mornings:
FRANKENSTEIN.

>   Now visible: MATE
>   (BELLAMY) and
>   FRANKENSTEIN, on the
>   ice.

FRANKENSTEIN

Ho!

MATE

Captain Walton, Sir!

WALTON

What is it, Mr. Bellamy?

MATE

A man, sir!

WALTON

Man overboard?

MATE

No sir. A man on the ice, sir. Difficult to
believe, I mean, hundreds of miles from the
nearest land, sir, and cold enough to freeze
the teats of a whale--

WALTON

For God's sake, Bellamy, get him aboard!

The Rope ladder is
thrown: FRANKENSTEIN
mounts.

*And cleaning out the Garbage. Put it in a truck that had not
been licensed since 1963. I found, by checking with the Chief of
Police, who drank at the Lexington Bar, that I didn't need it licensed
if I was going straight to the dump. Which was about thirty miles
away.*

*I went straight to the dump by about seventeen different
routes. In a sense they were straight – if I were a little confused
about where Lexington was.*

*I drove to the dump, many hundreds of times. I took old
bags, old stage sets, old I-don't-know-what–it–was and put it in the
Truck. When the Truck was full, off to the dump we would go. I was
told by the gentleman at the dump that I could dump free as long as
it was, mainly, garbage. It mainly was. The garbage of the people
around Lexington, who took it there, rather than to the dump.*

Ah, well.

*Printed in pale blue paint on one of the doors of the truck
was LEXINGTON. I added CONSERVATORY THEATRE.*

In Black Paint, which was all we had.

*I drove the unregistered Truck home through Hunter and
Haines Falls and Wyndham (where Steven Bock lived, who will be*

important later). Not that I went out much. Peanut Butter and Booze were what I lived on. And Camels.

   All this in Winter.

   Cold, and Lonely. And Hung-over.

   I wrote at the crack of dawn, before anyone was up.

   FRANKENSTEIN. Judy Martin's music helped, however I could play it.

                    FRANKENSTEIN
Forgive me, Henry. I am tired. I must sleep.
Meet me tomorrow. Here. Good Night.

                         FRANKENSTEIN goes to
                         sleep. In Darkness, the
                         CREATURE creeps into
                         FRANKENSTEIN's room.
                         FRANKENSTEIN tosses.

                    CREATURE
              (imitates FRANKENSTEIN)
Sleep.
                         HE lays hands on
                         FRANKENSTEIN tenderly.
                         FRANKENSTEIN wakes, and
                         screams.
Sleep.
                         HE pushes FRANKENSTEIN's
                         eyes shut with his hand,
                         then starts to climb
                         into the bed, like a
                         child. FRANKENSTEIN
                         screams again. HE leaps
                         out of the bed. The

```
                    CREATURE extends its
                    arms to him.
                    FRANKENSTEIN evades the
                    clutching hands and
                    bolts down the stairs.
Sleep!

                    It is a Pathetic Noise.
                    The CREATURE's hands
                    grope after the departed
                    FRANKENSTEIN.
```

My wife Meg was in New York City.
It was lonely. I worked. I thought about UBU REX.

I went walking. Strange place, Paris. But it seemed like home to me.

I discovered the Seine, its bars and knots of horseflesh, pigflesh.

Oh, I had friends: Marcel Schwob, Felix Feneon, Octave Mirbeau.

And I behaved like a very well-dressed Madman, for them.

By myself I was quieter, more studious.

The Barn Theatre, which I cleaned out first, stood nobly, all alone, on the hill above Lexington. Well, almost all alone. There was a had-once-been stable across the dirt road. Interesting place, kind of. It developed more Power as a place when we got a wine and beer license and set it up at the Blue Moon Cabaret. That was in '77.

I remember, among helpers, only Michael Hume, and possibly Steven Rotblatt. Hume and I took down the baseball seating that was in the barn. I am not sure what we did with it. It may have gone to the Dump. We got way more than two-hundred Theatre Seats, with padding, etc., from some Cinema that had gone broke.

Free.

Scavenging.

I went to school, the Henry IV, and one of my teachers was Bergson, in Psychology. I was studying to get a place at the École Normale Superieur, but for three years, despite my brilliance at Psychology, Arts, and Cosmology, I failed to get a place.

They didn't tell you things, the way they had at Rennes, they showed you how to discover it for yourself. We spent relatively little time in the classroom, and quite a lot of time in the Laboratories. It distinctly had its moments: as when M. Ris did a class on Sleep, and we stayed home, or when M. DuDin did a class on the Police, and was Arrested before the class even began.

At this time I was thinking seriously of becoming a Doctor of Research.

Which in a sense I still am. We still Are.

Researching 'Pataphysics, that which is as much beyond Metaphysics as Metaphysics is beyond Physics.

'Pataphysics.

You learn it: How to Deal, how to Work, how to Translate it into the Spectacles People Like.

Or, you don't.

Paris was curious, it was like a big village, with thousands of smells, hundreds of ways of dealing, in a city with a pig, or a horse. The Visions of Things, and the Smells, and the Sounds.

By the Seine: the Center of Paris, where there are many Brasseries, and horses tied up outside them. One rear leg raised, eating geraniums.

I began to draw them, in my — Style.

I began, despite my shyness, to meet people.

Not only Lesbics. I met people who mattered: Gauguin, with whom I stayed at Pont-Avon, Mallarmé, Picasso. Marcel Schwob, editor of *L'Echo de Paris*. Vallette, editor of the *Mercure de France*, and his wife, the novelist Mme Rachilde. It was a town — Paris — and the years in which the nuts of Symbolism were turning. And then I was a full-time student and a full-time member of the Symbolist ranks.

We looked like a collection of foreigners, all of whom came to Paris. And of course some of us even were Foreign.

Like Picasso.

I remember the rain in Paris fell straight down, not laid level by the winds.

And the Cafes. Literally hundreds of them.

My Mother moved to 84 Boulevard Pont-Royale.

She got me a space at 78 Boulevarde Pont-Royale. A studio, with a bed in it. Sometimes I stayed there on my own, sometimes I was Sent There.

Apparently I was Too Heavy on the guests. Too into whatever I was Into.

I was drawing, and writing. I was only, at that time, semi-obsessed with UBU.

I did strange things. Being admired for my Style in Latin, and asked by the Professor what Dead Latinate I used as a model. I said, "Aristophanes.'

The Class laughed, thinking I had confused the two, Latin and Greek. Then I patiently explained that I meant the translation into the discreet Latin of the obscene passages of the Ancient Greek, of Aristophanes.

That stopped the laughing.

And then I started my career as an Absintheur.

In the basement of the Hotel I found, early on, a lot of fifty-pound kegs of peanut butter. Had been sitting there for years, like from the end of World War II. It took me through that winter, that peanut butter, and took us a long way towards the end of Lexington. The barrels were there in 1978. They might still be there.

During my second year at school I met Leon-Paul Fargue. We had a similar quality of loving explorations, and I took him home and read him UBU ROI. Then we performed it, for fellow students, and hangers-on.

It was a Party-piece, and worked.

And of course Fargue played UBU.

Later we got things from the store in town, things the owner was going to throw away: milk, one day late, and usually quite sour; Wonder Bread, I don't know why, and Sausages, past their due date.

Occasionally he gave us something from the goodness of his German heart, like a bunch of carrots. What a heart.

I liked the Russian at the bar at the Hotel across the river much better. This Hotel was not abandoned, but not used very often either. Except for the Bar. He gave us, or Me, at any rate, a good deal of alcohol: Beer and Bourbon. Neither of them came to see anything at the Lexington Conservatory Theatre, although they only had to a walk across the Bridge.

Too bad.

It was the day I was celebrating the fact that I got into a College-Preparatory School that I discovered Absinthe. I was alone, walking with a slight spring in my step, and observing with an artist's eye the pair of horses, one dun, one almost pitch black, that were tied there, outside Le Rat Mort. The dun one seemed to have missed a joke, and was hanging its head, the black one had one rear leg cocked, and his head very high.

I didn't do what I normally did, which is guess the sex: the black horse had an Erection.

I looked where the black horse seemed to be looking, and saw a drinking establishment, Le Rat Mort. The Dead Rat. It looked undistinguished, and there were tables outside, with pairs of Women at them. The Women were curious, but I didn't at the time notice them. I went inside.

Long bar, many tables, light dim. Inside the place, no windows. Barkeep Female. Checker/Bouncer, a large Woman, in a Chair. Everywhere I looked, Femininity in all its guises. Women as Women, Women as Men, and Odd Ones.

All Female.

The Dead Rat became, after a time, one of may favorite hangouts, but it was quite evidently a Lesbic Bar.

And the Bouncer liked my —Style. I played Little-boy. I was a little boy, but I played Little-boy, and the Bouncer liked me, as did the Barkeep. I told the Bouncer about my College-Prep beauty of a day, and she indicated to the Bar-keep that everything today would be free, for me.

And the Barkeep said, "Shall we serve you Absinthe?"

The Bouncer said, "Have you had it?"

I had heard of it, but never had it. I said: "No."

The Barkeep said: "You will."

She poured Green Alcohol into a Metal Cup, posed a Flat Spoon across it and poured Sugar on it. The she added Water to the Green.

This is a great moment, a Beauty, and signals the beginning of a Habit. It is not a Habit I Hate, nor a Habit that has lost Me Anything, except the respect of the non-Absintheurs, and I don't care about them.

But the sheer beauty of setting up for Absinthe. Absinthe. Green. And pure Poison to the Taste Buds, so you pour Water in it through the Sugar. And then it tastes: Bad.

There, in The Dead Rat, a Lesbic Bar, I tasted my first drink of Absinthe.

And my Second.

Nota bene: Absinthe is probably the most Addictive substance in the world.

I experienced the Addictive nature of Alcohol.

Difficult to quit. I know.

There were two parts to being an Absintheur. The first is drinking it, which one did (then) everywhere. I picked bars like Le Rat Mort, where I sat, very quietly, working, and getting Absinthed. Looking at Dreams of Women.

Drinking Absinthe — one hundred and fifty proof alcohol, containing the Centre of Absinthe — Oil of Wormwood. Ah, Heaven! Ah, Hell.

The second part is the Adventures that arrive, or that one pulls onto one.

I forgot the third part; that comes later. The Massive, Uncontrollable Hallucinations, that take one over. I UBUed that one: I put muscle in my shoulders, broadened my stance, and Dumbed it.

"Ah," We said, to Mme Rachilde, "The Russians! The Czar of the Russians! He is sucking out Our Brain!"

We then Laughed, a Characteristic laugh.

Almost no note at that point about Alfred Jarry having hallucinations.

Because that was my Act. And so I played it.

In any case it is not Jarry having Hallucinations, it is UBU, played by Jarry, having Hallucinations.

But it is the one Dream I have, and continually, that I cannot Direct.

For a while it was exciting. Having a play take place that one does not direct. One thinks at first of God. But these were not God-given hallucinations. Or, if they were, God is a lot darker than we think him. Like Damballah-Wedo, the God of Voodoo, a Snake-God, a Black African God.

UBU as, well, Satan.

I had an office, but I was never, I repeat, never, there. Not once. I didn't even know where the office was. People, especially da Bouche, would bring me things, scripts, letters, from it.

I sometimes looked at them.

Vano had a small office, where he occasionally sat, for no reason that I could see, but he was Executive Director. I was Artistic Director, which meant, to me, that I spent most days fixing the goddamn plumbing.

And directing shows. Which Michael also did.

I was the first Acting Company member up there, so I had this kind of Father image. For a while. Then after I wrote FRANKENSTEIN I had this kind of image where, if you're nice to him he'll write you into a play. This on top of my Directing image, my Lighting (totally fake) image, and My Image. I was the one who never slept. You could find me on the Set, fixing Plumbing, Writing, or Drinking. That's about it. It took up twenty-four hours a day, and had there been Forty, it would have taken them up too.

1893. The 23rd of April, I published GUIGNOL, a UBIQUE piece, in a magazine called *L'Echo de Paris*. Marcel Schwob is the editor.

In my hooded, Provincial cape and my stovepipe hat I attended Mallarmé's last Tuesday soirees.

Where I would drink with Alfred Vallette, editor of the *Mercure de France*, and his novelist wife, the Beautiful Madame Rachilde.

The *Mercure's* parties had a higher class of writer. We, the new fellows, moved among them — Alfred Jarry, Andre Gide, Paul Valery: Checking, waiting.

My Voice became Well-Known.

*That first season I was directing on the Main Stage, HAIL
SCRAWDYKE, by David Halliwell, and, for our last show, my
adaptation of FRANKENSTEIN, with music by Judy Martin.*

*Somewhere in there, Off-Main Stage, I was throwing in
UBU REX.*

*By making a time and space for UBU to perform, we created
a Second Stage at Lexington. That was the beginning of PROVOS:
the Provisional Wing of LCT, our laboratory for new plays. New
plays – or new translations – which might or might not make it to
the Main Stage.*

*Some of those we tried out in PROVOS which did make it to
the Main Stage: Otis Bigelow's PREVALENCE OF MRS. SEAL
and Monty Merrick's NUSERYLAND; my own BEATRICE
(CENCI) AND THE OLD MAN and GRINDER'S STAND. Some
which didn't: William Sandwick & Theodore Soltanoff's brilliant
REVENGERS, a rock-musical adaptation of Tourneur's REVENGE
TRAGEDY, numerous plays by Paula Vogel, and many plays by
other playwrights, some of whom Went On.*

*Sometimes the season on the Second Stage was pretty good,
sometimes even better than what was the Main Stage.*

This caused some tumult, too.

*It was all originally based on UBU REX, which we were still
rehearsing. In fact, we never got out of rehearsing it.*

My Mother died. Tenth of May, 1893.

My Mother.

What did my Mother mean to me?

She meant a lot. She was short and soft, the definition
of everything, to me, Feminine, Maternal. It still makes me sad
to tell of her last days, her funeral. I was there, in my Top Hat,
my Hair growing Longer, weeping.

She meant something to me.

And she was so Soft.

She was very, very Bright.

That was May 10, 1893.

Preceded by forty days of her nursing me through a flu epidemic. I survived. Nine days later She Died, of a Sudden. This was a Strange Moment for me.

And very Sad.

And after that Alfred Jarry was UBU.

My father died in 1895. This did not bother me so much.

In this same year, 1893, Jarry finishes his translation of Coleridge's RIME OF THE ANCIENT MARINER. He meets Lord Alfred Douglas and, eventually, Oscar Wilde. He and his friends Fargue, Alfred Vallette, Madame Rachilde, Remy de Gourmont, attend openings of shows and are good supporters of Paul Fort's THEATRE D'ART.

This is a period when Paris is humming, almost bursting with ideas.

We have the Old and the New, meeting head on.

But with his mother dead, Jarry becomes much more of a Figure. And yet everyone said he was "shy."

But UBU is not shy.

O, No.

A Tuesday, Mallarmé-day. A Day when everyone who mattered would go to Mallarmé's and Be There. I showed up at Mme Rachilde's. Well dressed. Everything seemingly under control.

"Mme," I said, pronouncing every syllable with the same emphasis. "We would like to borrow your Yellow Pumps."

"You would," said Mme Rachilde. She was beautiful, childlike, eyes dark with Absinthe-memories.

"We would."

"Why?"

"The color Yellow strikes us as Beautiful."

So she lent them to Jarry. Yellow pumps, women's shoes, which he wore that day, causing a mild stir, as it was meant to.

Especially combined with the Guns that Jarry wore, outside his costume. And his Absinthe. And his American cigarettes.

Was Jarry making a statement? I don't think so. It's just an extending out, from Inside Himself, of Ubique Reality. "Le Parler Ubu," a way of speaking where everything was described; for instance, a Bicycle is "that which rolls."

Ubu published, disguised as Jarry, a piece in which he claims the invention of "Carpet Slippers": an inexpensive way to have carpet under your feet without having actual carpet in rooms, like in the bathroom, where it might get wet. Ubu gives himself credit for inventing Carpet Slippers.

As I developed the character, "Jarry," I was also going to School. Living, until March, 1893, with my Mother. It was in

1893, the year My Mother died, that I met Lord Alfred
Douglas.

He had the same first name as me.

This was not interesting.

*Well, finally it was Arrival Days, and I got my Volvo and
ferried the actors from the Bus Station in Hunter to Lexington
Conservatory Theatre. It was kind of fun. Michael Hume came early.
Van Landingham and Wendy Chapin and Bouchard and Nesbit
came next. Zobel had his truck, and neglected to drive anybody up
from NYC in it. And there were Sofia Landon, and Kate Kelly, and
Laralu Smith. Miriam Layn, an older, handsome, ex-Broadway-ite,
arrived in a Cadillac, because she was an ex-Theatre person who'd
married well.*

*Hume and Nesbit became friends, and opted to room
together. Zobel built a tree house. Steve Rotblatt, small, Jewish, and
Kristin Joliff, a handsome Southern-California blonde, both good
actors, weren't married then, though they became so, and they took
the first of the lower cabins, by the River Theatre.*

*No bathrooms. That was the first, and it turned out, eternal
problem. There weren't any bathrooms. The entire Theatre Company
depended on one bathroom, upstairs in the hotel. It had a Shower in
it too, and people used to sign up to use it. Weeks in advance.*

*Actually there were three toilets: the one in the Hotel, one for
the audience in the Barn Theatre, and one for the audience in the
River Theatre. So there were three places they could go to urinate,
when they hadn't urinated in the bushes. But only one shower.*

*Then came people complaints: Nesbit and Hume decided
they couldn't, after all, room together. There were huge verbal
shouting matches at three in the morning, until Hume moved to a
bottomless geodesic Dome, and strung a hammock there.*

Michael van Landingham moved to a dorm. Miriam Layn took the other one.

Kate Kelly and Michael Hume had a torrid-seeming affair, which may have been interesting, with Hume living in that bottomless Geodesic Dome.

Steve Nesbit, who was carrying on a gay life in NYC, was having an affair with Forbesy, a woman. They wound up living in the cardboard-shielded attic of the Blue Moon Cafe, where there were people literally twenty-four hours a day.

Anyway, we opened the season with OUR TOWN, and people came, though we had budgeted no money to pre-season advertising.

Next, in the River Theatre, we did CHARLEY'S AUNT, with an absolutely Heavenly performance by Steven Nisbet. The Utter Mess of the Scrawdyke Set – the next production – was going into the Barn. Designed by Me, it was an attempted recreation of my work-space in NYC.

Before we started drawing people up from NYC to see the shows, our audience consisted of people who knew some theatre, who were summering in this strange part of the Catskills, and who read our very small ads in the local paper.

They came, and the actors were great and the set was good and lighting and sound and everything worked well. We were fine, all happy, and we had no money.

And it was a dicey time to consider opening HAIL SCRAWDYKE, by David Halliwell, and a really, really dicey time to consider opening UBU REX.

So, of course, I considered both, and got to work.

My mother died.

We lost track of reality for a while, after our Mother died.

We got it back through UBU.

That is, Jarry (I) became UBU (We). Or UB (We).

UB. Picked up as the result of a conversation with Mme Rachilde, and so Me — Us. It would make sense if Jarry (I) had created UB, but he didn't. Not in any real sense.

Of course I could say: UB Exists.

And the strange thing is, I would be right. Not only is there an UBU who appears at various times and places on the stage, there is also UB — Ourself. We look like a Short Man in a Top Hat and UBU Costume, but we are More. We are the Inventor of Carpet Slippers. We are the Man who overpowers Mother Ubu. We are UB.

The Ubique Company (me) got right onto re-doing UBU REX.

Some of it was already cast. We had Richard Zobel as UBU.

I had always liked Steven Rotblatt, but I liked him, now, in an Ubique sense. He had intense focus on the stage. I cast him as MOTHER UBU.

Also, he did drawings of the show, and they were good. We used them for the poster.

Winship Cook, who had studied Mime with Etienne Decroux, could puppetize anything using her body, and had an incredible ability to play weird parts. I loved the rehearsals that would become shouting matches between her and Steve Rotblatt: rather, he would shout and she would strike a pose indicating her response. He would complain, but he knew she was good.

Wendy Chapin Stage-managed UBU REX. *She also Stage-managed* HAIL, SCRAWDYKE. HAIL, SCRWDYKE *is very funny, and very destructive. It takes place in the northern part of*

England, almost Scotland, so we had accents that were, at first, almost undecipherable. And in this other-language, Scrawdyke almost Monologues the entire show.

Michael Hume was praised for his depiction of Scrawdyke, a crazy man who talks himself into suicide and does it. With the edge of open tin can. On Stage.

And now it was time to open UBU REX.

Jarry, I, was relatively intelligent. Relatively shy. A nice, handsome, Short Boy. UBU was different. UBU was powerful, a man who, Dumbly, made his way from being Captain of Dragoons in Poland, a Country that did not then, Legally Exist, to being King of the World.

That's pretty good.

Merdre.

Our first season at LCT, 1976, we made a mistake.

Because so many of our actors, like Bruce Bouchard, Michael Hume, Steven Nesbit were Equity (Union), and because we couldn't pay them Equity wages, we had to give them something, and what we gave them was the right to approve shows, and directors, and even actors.

O No.

Poor idea.

They watched the rehearsals of the first show, OUR TOWN, and approved, but by the time we got to HAIL SCRAWDYKE (or "Little Malcolm and his Struggle Against the Eunuchs"), they were not so kind. They wanted Hume to play Scrawdyke, and so did I. But they didn't like it when I cast Zobel as his friend the weird Wick.

So they attended rehearsals and Talked Loudly during Zobel's scenes.

So I had the rehearsals categorized as Private.

They fought me on this. But I liked Zobel as a performer, and I didn't want him getting the ideas that They didn't like him. Not that it would have mattered to Richard Zobel.

I went into the Theatre Company's Artistic Directorship a Socialist, and came out of it an Absolute Tyrant. They would either do it my way, or no way.

There is an UBU. I became him — but also he Exists.

SCRAWDYKE was up and running. Now, UBU.

Would the Audience understand Jarry? Would they understand that I was trying, in my direction of the Play, to make all the actors be Puppets?

Our venue for UBU was the River Theatre, on the OUR TOWN set. We had our lights: One Fresnel, Dead White in Color. We had our Masks, our Costumes. But would the Acting work?

Would they see?

Merdre.

I think it was the day after we opened HAIL SCRAWDYKE that we opened UBU REX.

Zobel, Wick in SCRAWDYKE, played UBU. And played him well.

Despite Company Quarrels.

The people who came to see UBU REX knew UBU as a Theatre-Problem. And they loved it. There weren't very many of them, but they came back. And laughed uproariously.

This was a relief to me. First the long hesitation before storms of applause in HAIL, SCRAWDYKE. Then laughter for UBU REX. Laughter means they Understood it. Good.

Jarry may not have found UBU REX very funny, but everyone who matters since has.

Our audiences found it funny, and Applauded quite loudly, it seemed to me.

Good.

Absinthe put me in the UBU space, but also I met a Fragment of Him when I joined the Military, for a while. Or actually, was "Drafted."

The Fragment of UBU was a Corporal.

As long as we're passing around stories of Military Servitude: I was drafted in 1968. I had just turned 18, we had the Lottery, and I got No. 1. I dressed as a Lunatic Hippy and went by bus to Auburn, thence to Oakland, where I Refused Induction.

There were quite a few Refusers that day, and I guessed, most every day, despite the fact that they offered the choice: Two Years in Vietnam or Four Years in Prison.

I chose Prison.

But because I was 18, rather than 18 1/2, I beat the system.

I went to Europe for a number of years, but I knew that if I came home, I would be Drafted again.

And somehow, I felt like Jarry.

Sometimes.

I was called up in 1894. November 13th. 101st Regiment of Artillery. Laval. A corporal named Bouilly took charge of me and tried to get me to do KP and clean up. Needless to say he failed. Very Ubique, was Bouilly. Half-human, others would call him, but to me he was UBU.

"So!" said Bouilly. "You are of a child's height."

"But an adult's brain. Sir."

"Brains don't matter here, kid. Physical size, that matters."

"I'm sorry. Sir." I intoned. I was, in fact, not sorry at all.

"Can you drink?" asked Bouilly.

"Yes, sir. Absinthe."

So we started drinking Absinthe. That's We and Bouilly.

As I remember it, the Judge, a woman, said, "Well, Mr. Hall, why won't you go fight a Legal War in Vietnam?"

"Well, Your Honor," I said. "Begging your pardon. It is not a Legal War. It is a Police Action."

"No, Mr. Hall," she said, Mildly. Pompously. "It is a Legal War."

"I don't think it is a Legal War, Your Honor."

"Court Recorder," she asked the man with the little machine. "Is it a Legal War, or a Police Action?"

He looked up. "Uh," he said. "Actually, Your Honor, it is a Police Action."

"Really?" said the Judge, looking amazed. "Well, then. Case Dismissed."

I looked at her for a long time, picked up my coat, walked out of the Induction Center, took my Porsche 914 to Reno, and flew to London.

Although it is true that I took a bus to get to Oakland.

I don't remember this period very well either. And I'm told I have it Wrong.

There was also a first drummer. Bols might have been his name, who tried to keep up with my already growing capacity for Absinthe.

He, too, failed.

I was mustered out on the basis of Precocious Imbecility.

Which is a long way of saying that they couldn't teach me anything.

Not in bloody Laval.

In Warsaw, maybe. Not in Laval.

Note: Actually, Jarry was dismissed from Military Servitude for "Chronic Lithiasis' (Gallstones), not "Precocious Imbecility." It is interesting that Jarry buys into Jarry's own Myth. Jarry brought his bicycle, got a large quantity of hydrochloric acid to clean it, and then drank the hydrochloric acid, and almost committed suicide.

Apparently, to Jarry, the "Potache," the overqualified Bum, the Army was a Vacation. And in effect, it was. Except for the Suicide Attempt, and even that might have been Vacation-thinking for Jarry. Or it may have been a reaction to being an alcoholic, which he was.

He also got, from his brief stint in the Army, a book: LES JOURS ET LES NUITS.

I wrote LES JOURS ET LES NUIT about my mishap-prone life in the Military. How our life is a dream, and dreams our life. How Absinthe dictates everything I do and say. If I drink it.

If I don't — Pssssssshhhhht!

With my Mother Dead, my Family started to go like flies. The Fourth of February, 1894, Papa Quernest, Mother's Father, died. In 1895, my own Father died.

Also in that year the *Mercure de France* published two sections of my CESAR-ANTÉCHRIST, and then on the First of October, 1895, published the whole Book.

But I became suffused with the oil of UBU. He became a kind of God to me. Lacking my Mother. Who was Dead. And who was, when Alive, the real MOTHER UBU. She was My Mother, and at the same time, she was MOTHER UBU.

I can't explain this, it is simply true.

I took the Porsche 914 to the Reno Airport and left it there forever. I flew to England. Dana was already there, and we came together. It was nice.

It got a little weird in there because I was still trying to make it as a Lead Guitar Player, and everyone in Music who Mattered in London was Gay.

So I, briefly, became Gay.

And Dana went off to Corfu.

'Pataphysics noted, somewhere, as Art/Anarchy.

Merdre.

I had a lot of money at this point in my life. My Mother died — sadness — My Grandfather died.

I took an apartment at 162 Boulevard St.-Germain. I took to lying around a great deal, bouncing chick-peas off the hats of passers-by. And other traditional Just-Inherited-A-Lot-Of-Money Pastimes.

I built a stage, and did UBU ROI, as a Puppet-show, for our friends.

Dana went off and I stayed in London, liking the Blues, the London Way of Life, the Five O'clock Fogs.

I got a rich, American set of Twin Gays, though I only slept with one of them.

A fellow named Lugne-Poe had taken over Paul Fort's THEATRE D'ART. Lugne-Poe renamed it THE THEATRE DE L'OEUVRE.

I was taken up, in May, by Lugne-Poe and the Theatre de l'Oeuvre, as a kind of Secretary. They were good, the Theatre de l'Oeuvre. Loose, smart, and under Lugne-Poe, very Avant-garde.

Although then I met the French Girl with Gold on her Hands.

Lugne-Poe claimed to be a descendant of Edgar Allan, although I doubted this. I worked for him as a top-hatted Secretary, being in charge of some things. I proposed that the Oeuvre produce Ibsen's PEER GYNT, partly adapted by me, and my play UBU ROI.

Thus began the search for a director, and I settled on Lugne-Poe.

Which was handy, because I was working for him.

Note: This is a nice story, but might be an error. Another version of this story is simply that Lugne-Poe read UBU ROI, liked it, and decided to produce — and direct — it.

PEER GYNT was relatively easy to cast, with me — Jarry — as Troll of the Court. I liked, from that experience, Lugne-Poe as a director. He was interested in, and the show was interested in, what people did, rather than the surreal text. PEER GYNT opened and ran, but despite Jane Avril in the cast, and Munch's work on the Sets, and myself in the cast, PEER GYNT was a dirge at the box office. Which made me err, in selecting it. Ah, well.

Then Lugne-Poe started thinking about UBU ROI.

The Girl who rescued me from the Sherlock Holmes' Fog of London on my flight from the Draft, and took me to Paris, was a Gold Smuggler. She went around, in her tight Levi's, with her Pockets full of gold. Not Gold made into Coins: pre-Human Gold. Flakes, strange growths of Gold, in her Pockets.

She was nineteen, and French, and her brother smuggled Gold into France, from Africa.

I was not doing much, lounging in St. James's Park, my hands in the pockets of my too-tight cords, not thinking about anything but the pain in my Homosexual Asshole, when this beautiful, full-Breasted girl, in Levi's and a work shirt, approached me. She was handsome, and wore gold-rimmed dark glasses.

She came and looked at the same tree I was not looking at.

"You have no cigarettes for Girl you Met in Park?" she said in her husky, French-accented voice.

I looked at her, nodded, and pulled a pack of Player's from my breast pocket. I gave us each one, and lit them with matches.

"You are French," I said, brilliantly.

"Oui," she said, pulling on her cigarette. "From Paris, now."

"Ah," nodding, as if this meant anything to me.

I noticed then the strange gleaming lumps on her hands. The hands were quite beautiful, rings here and there and Lumps of Shining Stuff on them. I took her hand and looked at it closer. I looked into her face.

She had her Player's stuck in her mouth and around it she said, "Gold."

"Gold?" I said. I held onto her hand. She was, after all, a female, and I hadn't seen one in a while.

She put her other hand in her pocket and brought out lumps of Gold: "Gold."

We went to a British bar. I had French wine. She had American Beer. She told me that she smuggled in Gold her brother had stolen from a camp where he worked, in Morocco. She made a pretty good living at this, selling Gold to, as she called them: "Odd-Shops."

I gave her another cigarette, and told her about my life, unexpurgated.

She giggled. "So," she said, cigarette in her mouth, angling a look at me from her faded blue eyes, "You want to go to Paris?"

UBU ROI was a nightmare of casting. We finally got Firmin Gemier from the Comédie Française to play UBU, which made Lugne-Poe happy, and as MOTHER UBU, Louise France. Of whom I approved, as I did not Gemier.

On UBU ROI Lugne-Poe as a Director was another cup of tea. Or tin-glass of Absinthe. He knew nothing about the Play and Did Not Learn from it.

"UBU's about life in Poland," said Lugne-Poe, in his introduction to the play.

One could quibble with this. After all, at the time, there was no Poland.

Louise France looked at him, her pen in her hand, her rehearsal dress in a state of readiness. Firmin Gemier looked arrogant.

"And therefore," said Lugne-Poe, "I want you all to study Polish People."

Well, there we were.

UBU's about UBU. And MOTHER UBU. And our conceptions of what the Set looked like.

Not the Text, which is joke-oriented.

Lugne-Poe was working from the Text, from the idea that the UBUs were a Normal Family, in Surreal Circumstances.

And that's wrong.

It's a Surreal Family, in Normal Circumstances.

The first edition of one of Jarry's last published works, a one-act comic morality play intended as a series of six. The final four were never published because of his death in 1907, at age 27.

So I went to Paris. With the Girl with Gold on her
Hands. She indicated that we could leave everything with
my — well — clients, with the exception of my Passport. I
carried my Passport in my rear pants pocket, and showed it to
her. She took it, and gurgled at the boy in the photograph.

"Si jeune," she said, husking.

*So we took the six PM boat from England to France. She
paid for things when I couldn't. She lived in the Sixth
Arrondisement, and she drove a Deux-Cheveaux. These are
apparently cars that have Two Horse-Power. Two.*

*She parked it on the sidewalk, and mainly drove it on the
sidewalk. "To avoid the other Autos," she said. When she parked it,
she always left the keys in it. It was not much of a struggle to replace
it. They cost Sixty Dollars, new.*

*One day we decided to go to a ski area. We got our
equipment, mainly hers, and got into the Deux-Cheveaux, and
started to drive. You know French Freeways, you go as fast as you
can. Everybody else was doing over a Hundred miles per Hour. We
were doing about Two miles per Hour. Everybody else got there in a
couple of hours. It took us six days.*

*There was her brother, bringing in pounds of Gold, her
mother, and friends, including a Russian Trotskyite.*

Trotsky?

*This was, in Jarry's terms, a Surreal Family, in Normal
Circumstances.*

Lugne-Poe had long moustachios, and stroked them.
Gernier asked him what voice Lugne-Poe wanted for UBU,

and Lugne-Poe said, "You hear the voice of the Author? Imitate that, and we'll all be fine."

I ask you.

Lugne-Poe asked people how he should direct UBU ROI, and Mme Rachilde, the great somewhat freaky novelist told him, "En Guignol."

Note: "As a masked farce."

So we did it that way. Which made me happy.

Masks are crucial to my concept of Theatre. The only thing we have now is the antique Italian Theatre, Commedia del Arte, done in the old way with Masks. But those masks are so very refined.

I wanted UBU to be masked, and He is not refined at all. Nor is anyone with Him.

Basically Children's Nightmares, and Masked.

I have dreams where Everyone is Masked. Nightmares, too.

UBU, and RICHARD III and FAUSTUS. All Masked.

And when they remove them, nothing there. A Blank Face.

I got to know the Actors, some in this way, some in others. Michael Hume (the J came when he joined Equity), for example, though he was at that time a Drinker, maybe even a Big Drinker, was always calm, thoughtful, wise. Young as I was, he was two years younger. Kate Kelly, who played the woman in HAIL

SCRAWDYKE, was alternately brilliant and deeply flawed. Steve
Nesbit was split between his Musical Theatre background and very
modern, very bad drug-taking. He was fine as an actor, it you knew
how to use him and how to treat him. Sofia Landon was always
brilliant, an actress who never had a bad moment on stage. James
Rice, another brilliant actor, underused by us. Steve Rotblatt,
Kristin Joliff. All excellent actors.

    OUR TOWN: It was probably a good start to the first
season. A little gloomy, and short on action. But it showed some
actors off and that was good.

    CHARLEY'S AUNT: Steve Nesbit was great. I was in it,
and I remember going after the show came down to working on the
set for HAIL SCRAWDYKE.

    SCRAWDYKE's words were beautiful, poignant, violent, I
basically watched for things that worked, and kept them. Kate was
great, they all were, but they paled beside Hume as Scrawdyke.

    I don't remember much about THE ENCHANTED.

    And then came FRANKENSTEIN.

My best friend through these rehearsals and etc. was
Vallette, Editor of the *Mercure*. Married to the Arcane novelist
Mme Rachilde. She was much taller than he. I often ate dinner
at their place. Mme Rachilde didn't cook, and Vallette
couldn't, so we bizarred it through. Vallette and I bicycled and
fished and boated and fenced together. Mme Rachilde and I
Absinthed.

I made Trout a lot, Which I also caught.

I was very good at catching Trout.

Vallette was an editor, and an inspiration to young
writers. A good friend.

Mme Rachilde. She was, well, Big. Bigger then Vallette,
and he was fairly tall. I rather enjoyed going on a walk with

her, with my top hat on, which might have reached her chin. We talked UBIQUE — she it was whose idea it was to call me UB, Not UBU, UB.

"Ah, Ub," she would say, precisely, "Let's go absorb alcohol."

"Eh, if you wish, Mme," We said.

So we went. Absinthing.

I, having opened two plays, HAIL, SCRAWDYKE and UBU REX, was tired.

And I had still to work on FRANKENSTEIN. In fact, I had to Write it, and Stage it, and Light it, and Set it. I was faintly bummed.

But happy. I felt, at that point, that if Jarry could have come back and seen us there, laboring at Theatre in a small farm in Lexington, New York, he'd have been pleased.

If we had Absinthe.

Louise France was great as MOTHER UBU. And all the Littles were great. But Gemier. For one thing he wouldn't wear a Mask. So we made him up, Dead White, with three little Black Spots, indicating his Moustache. He used a voice with Two Tones in it, a pretty good imitation of mine.

He walked out on stage, after my introductory messages, and looked around, and said, "Merdre."

That was the First Line of the Play, and brought the audience to their feet. Some were applauding that "Mot de Cambronne" that opened the show. Most of them, though, were booing, and hissing.

It took almost half an hour to get through Scene One. Which is under two pages in length. The Critics were all there, and they were a kind of Ubique study: Bored, Enraged, Happy at the Total Meaninglessness of the Text.

It was a fair description of what happened with the Critics in the reviews. It was almost like Baby-talk, their reviews.

The ones who liked UBU ROI liked it for the wrong reasons. Childish reasons. The ones who hated it, hated it for the wrong reasons too: again, Childish.

UBU ROI is not a Childish Play. It is relatively Sophisticated.

Merdre.

Note: Mot de Cambronne has to do with a General of Napoleon's, who said "Merde" when faced with an impossible situation. I think he later won.

This story also reminds me, though I don't know why, of when Mandy Patinkin and Peter Clough optioned MIKE FINK, for a year, and they somehow got it put on, as a Reading, at the Public Theatre, for the eyes of People and Joseph Papp.

This would have been between two LCT seasons, the winter of '77.

Joseph Papp was a kind of God amongst grant-getters, and was turning out a fine bunch of actors, too. Peter Clough directed, and Mandy Patinkin played MIKE FINK.

They claimed to have auditioned all through New York City, and Mandy was the rightest person they could find. I doubted this, but was so excited to have my Major Verse Drama done for Joseph Papp, who ran the New York Shakespeare Festival, that I buried my doubts.

It was a poor reading. Mandy was all right, but way Too Short for the part. Papp left half-way through the first act.

And it had Five Acts.

But it was fun to be hooked up with Papp's Play-searching. He was looking hard for new Plays, and new Directorial Aims.

It was what I wanted to do at Lexington.

I wanted to Blow the Theatre Apart, by Making New.

Vallette and Mme Rachilde came to Opening Night. Of course UBU only ran two nights, although Lugne-Poe said it would be kept in their Repertoire, to be done again. He assured me it would be done again.

It wasn't.

Anyway, they came to Opening Night. We were out in the lobby, Ubique. Hips low, bent forward, head high. We greeted people, in our Machinist Speech. Each critic looked like who he was: neckties, top hats, clothes gotten off the street, you know.

I drank Wine, Ubique-style, and smoked.

At a certain point Lugne-Poe got people in and Me up on Stage. I gave my ten minutes of two-tone weirdness, ending with, "as to the Action, it takes place in Poland, which is to say: Nowhere."'

Some applause.

Drank Absinthe, non-Ubique style.

My adaptation of FRANKENSTEIN wasn't, surprisingly, the horror story everyone expects from the title. It is the story of a Very Young Man, Frankenstein's CREATURE, looking for his Father, Victor Frankenstein. From the day of his birth, he kills only One person who is not a Frankenstein, and she is a Maid of the

Frankensteins. All of the CREATURE's actions are efforts to persuade Victor that he is no Creature but a Human Being.

                         TWO: 2:
                         Enter CREATURE.

                    CREATURE

Frankenstein.

                         FRANKENSTEIN
                         hesitates, then
                         attacks him. The
                         CREATURE easily
                         overpowers him.

                    CREATURE

I should have expected this reception. Even
you, my maker, detest me.

                    FRANKENSTEIN

If only by unmaking you I could restore Life
to your victims!

                    CREATURE

How you sport with Life, Frankenstein. You
created me. Why? What was your intention? You
fabricated me. I know the whole disgusting
story, but I cannot guess the motive. God made
Adam, as you made me, punished and abandoned
him, as you have done to me. but . . . Adam
disobeyed! Adam transgressed . . . I never
did. From the moment of my birth I was
abandoned: you never gave me any command but
one: Sleep, you said, and now I understand
that you meant Die! Is this the sin that I am

```
punished for? Not dying? If my existence is a
crime, it is your crime, not mine, and I will
not die to rectify it.
                    (FRANKENSTEIN buries
                    his head in his
                    hands)
Listen to me, Frankenstein. I am your child,
your creation. You owe me . . . you owe
me . . . LOVE.
```

Unfortunately, the Creature is Twice the Size of a Human Being, and has scars indicating his "Birth."

I pre-cast both Hume and Sofia Landon in FRANKENSTEIN. Hume's role was good. Sofia's was the Bride of Victor Frankenstein. It always struck me, in the movies, or other adaptations of the story, as a role that was under-rehearsed, or underplayed, or something. But maybe there's just something wrong with the part. The Action is elsewhere, most of the time, so it's not Crucial.

The Set, designed by me, was made of scaffolding and had a section three stories tall and many small spaces, which gave Michael Hume, the CREATURE, places to Wait, to Look.

And it you have every watched a Baby, you know that for the first year, or two years of their life, they are Learning Machines. So I had Frankenstein's Creature Watching. Learning. Tremendous shadows, as this Twice-the-Size-of-a-Human-Being Looked.

The rest of the show was Seamy: Turn of the Century Weird. Subtle Violence. And I had Judy Martin's music.

In the end the Monster vows to Captain Walton to go to the North Pole and Freeze Solid so he won't menace Earth any more.

Michael Hume, who developed a tremendous quietness to his movements, was great as Frankenstein's CREATURE.

The critics rioted from the first line: "MERDRE," and then continued to riot through the whole Play. It lasted, unusually, hours, and at the end of the play, the Theatre was in ruins. We put it back together for the next night.

I had meant to write down what the Critics said: "Oh! Theatre is Dead," etc. But I was too much of a mess to do it. Absinthe, Tabac, and Nerves.

The reviews were about what we thought they would be.

The audience was a little quieter the Second night.

It reminded people of the opening night of HERNANI, by Victor Hugo.

It reminded me of a Bad Absinthe Night: Bad taste, and not much else.

Opening night of FRANKENSTEIN.

First Year of Lexington Conservatory Theatre. Last show of the Season.

On his first professional Opening Night, Jarry got Absinthed. On mine I met with the cast before the show. We all knew they were terrifically under-rehearsed. I said, "Go for it. You all know what we are trying to do. So do it. I love you all."

Then I took LSD.

I was pretty much Stage Manager and would be running lights and sound. I took the Acid at the beginning of the Play, spoke to the Audience, and started running the Show. I loved things about it, its shadows, its strangely costumed People, and I had managed to get the Forty-track tape of Judy's music down to Ten Tracks, and knew when to amplify beats, go silent, go with a full Seventeenth Century instrumental Track. It was a beautiful show to watch, from

Gretchen Van Ryper as a dirty peasant, to Steve Nesbit, as Victor Frankenstein, in a beautiful seventeenth-century suit; from Michael Hume as the Creature to the bare expanses of snow. Lights, Sound. And knowing when to crank Sound so it would cover the fact that very few actors actually knew their lines.

I bumped out the lights at the end of the Show, put them up again for Curtain Call, and then went out, clambering, on the Three Story Set, and spoke to the Audience again, thanking them, and invited them to the Cabaret, an old Horse-barn where I paid for everybody's First Drink.

I embraced Steve Nesbit and Hume and said, "We did it."

And Hume looked at me, part Hume and part Frankenstein's Creature, and said, "But of Course." Then he Grinned.

It was a good show: About Father-Craving and yet not about Father-Craving. And it turned into a Horror-Tale, even though it wasn't.

And the Audience response to FRANKENSTEIN indicated very strongly that they (the Audience) Liked New Plays.

This was good.

Bless William Butler Yeats, the Irish poet, who loved UBU ROI, and said it was something new in Comedy. He covered it with praise.

Unfortunately, he didn't understand French, and he wrote about it for some paper in Dublin, and by the time the review appeared the play had closed.

I have this occasional fantasy that I will end up in Dublin and they will all know me, because Yeats liked UBU ROI.

"Ah, yes, You're Alfred Jarry, author of UBU ROI!"
will say an Irish bar-keep. "Have a beer, free, my little 'Savage
God'."

Beer. Because I know for a fact, from Yeats himself,
that they don't have Absinthe there.

*We didn't know we were good until something like the
middle of the run of FRANKENSTEIN. We just didn't know.
Evelyn Weisberg, the woman who rented us the Lexington property,
had a mother-in-law who came to every performance of
FRANKENSTEIN. At the Closing Night Party she said she had
never been so affected by a Theatre Piece in her life. And she'd seen
many. She looked at me with her eyes starting to tear.*

"This is Great Theatre," she said.

I was moved.

*There was a small amount of pressure to try to open
FRANKENSTEIN on Broadway, but I wasn't interested. Way, way
too big a gamble. A year later someone else did it, with another
adaptation based on the novel. It did poorly.*

*I thought of this as a We/I problem. We – Lexington
Conservatory Theatre – versus I – Oakley Hall III.*

And I decided for the We.

We thought about Death quite a bit. Because in the
Theatre you have Opening Day, and Closing Day, and UBU
had already Opened, and would Close the next day.

Whenever that was, but "Next Day" indicated: Soon.

The day after the opening of UBU ROI, we had to put
the theatre back together for the second night. This audience
wasn't so wild, not having any critics in its make-up.

*By this time I was using Alcohol as a basis for whatever I
did. And then I would get stoned, smoking marijuana or hashish on
top of whatever I'd drunk.*

*But I never got stoned and sat. Just as, I think, Jarry never
got Absinthed and sat. I would get stoned and Write, or get stoned
and Design a Set, or get stoned and Wander around New York City.*

*And that is where I got the strange ideas that modified
Lexington Conservatory Theatre into slightly Avant, or Arriere-
garde. One or two New Plays in a six-play season, was one of my
ideas. This is tough, as Plays don't Develop until, as they say,
they've been "On the Boards" for a while.*

*Our first season, 1976, we produced OUR TOWN,
CHARLEY'S AUNT, HAIL SCRAWDYKE, a children's show,
PORTABLE ANNABEL, THE ENCHANTED, and my adaptation
of FRANKENSTEIN.*

*For the 1977 season I picked some Antique Weirdness, à la
Ford's 'TIS PITY SHE'S A WHORE, and a New Weirdness, Otis
Bigelow's PREVALENCE OF MRS. SEAL. Also some Wholesome,
THE TAVERN. Vano wanted to direct QUALITY STREET.*

*And running concurrently was Provos Theatre: readings of
new plays, productions of new plays, productions of not-yet-
established plays, my translations of the Ubu plays, and UBU REX.*

THE WINDHAM JOURNAL, Thursday, July 7, 1977

LCT Provos, the experimental wing of the
Lexington Conservatory Theatre, has announced its first
production, Alfred Jarry's UBU REX. UBU REX is the
work of a Frenchman, Alfred Jarry, an alcoholic midget who
was the grandfather of surrealist theatre. Jarry apparently
wrote UBU REX while in high school; when the play was
first produced in Paris in 1896 there were riots in the
theatre — the critics were either enraged or baffled.

The play is written as a "Punch-and-Judy" show, and translator-director Oakley Hall has staged it that way as well. The faces of the actors are hidden by amazing masks, designed by Richard Zobel, who also plays the role of Ubu.

Sheer slapstick lunacy for broadminded children of all ages.

We did UBU REX as part of Provos for the First Three of Lexington's seasons. It was successful, and we got Elements from it, both as Directors and as Actors, to use in other shows, like FRANKENSTEIN and 'TIS PITY, and virtually all of Giraudoux's THE ENCHANTED.

Our reviews, except for Yeats's, were quite terrible. The Avant-gardists liked it, but for all the wrong reasons. UBU ROI is a Puppet show. Nobody got this, with the exception of maybe Yeats, whose review I didn't read, not getting the Dublin paper.

I , We, became, however, even better known.

Jarry is becoming known.

For (1) being an Absintheur, and (2) being always in Costume and the Mood to play UBU. These two things make him known and understood and publicized in newspaper columns.

And of course he was called UB, or UBU.

There is a great deal of information on UB or UBU. Very little on Jarry.

This may be intentional. Or may not.

I knew different people, too. Toulouse-Lautrec, for one. He was also short in size. A Dwarf, they said. Toulouse-Lautrec said, "No, friend, not a dwarf." He showed me his legs.

They were very short and didn't look like legs at all.

"They're calcimined," Toulouse-Lautrec said. "I am from the great old family of the Toulouse-Lautrec-Monfa's, but I have always been, ah, Tiny."

He painted, sculpted, and worked in the Theatre. In fact, that's where I met him, doing UBU ROI.

Season 77.

We opened with THE TAVERN, a traditional summer stock play, with weirdnesses. The weirdnesses were Hume's (who played the Vagabond), and Steve Patterson's, who directed. It was fun. It had a Tavern, built by me, into which blew the Vagabond, and then the trouble starts. The play started the season off with a bang, which is good, because it was succeeded by Inge's PICNIC, a show I hadn't picked, and about which I had some serious negative thoughts. I didn't like the director, Bill Herndon, but I am not sure why.

I have a memory of Herndon driving up from NYC, day before opening, with his Madge, played by my sister, Sands. He arrived late at night at the River Theatre, where PICNIC's set was just being completed. He drove into the driveway and shined his lights into the building. Steven Nesbit was standing there, grinning, having just painted the entire set — three houses plus — red. Red. A realistic set. Herndon did not say anything for a long time. I smoked, and watched.

THE WINDHAM JOURNAL, Thursday, July 21, 1977

The Lexington Conservatory Theatre complex has undergone another transformation: now they're wandering around in flowing robes and scabbards, flashing swords in the sunlight and speaking in grand tones. Preparation for the LCT production of *'Tis Pity She's a Whore* is underway. This is the first of LCT's classical productions, directed by Oakley Hall III, who wrote and directed *Frankenstein* last summer. Many members of the LCT company have received extensive training in the classics, and now they will have an opportunity to use it. Classical drama requires grueling work if it is to be good: voice lessons are given daily, as are movement classes and warm up exercises, and rehearsals stretch far into the night.

Oakley Hall III, the artistic director of LCT, is a man of letters, whose play, *Mike Fink*, was recently read at the Public Theatre in New York for Joseph Papp. One look at Oakley reveals the intensity of his vision, and the quality of the theatre he creates (*Frankenstein, Hail Scrawdyke* and *UBU REX*, which is playing this weekend) reveals his preoccupation with the gripping, the entertaining, the bizarre.

'TIS PITY came next. It's a psychological Elizabethan drama that was banned in England for something like one hundred and fifty years because the two lovers at the center of the play are brother and sister (Steve Patterson and Sofia Landon). But incest was a small aspect of the show. I directed, and using a great deal of stage blood, killed off the entire cast of the show by the end, except for the Cardinal (played by Me) who has to say the line, "'tis pitty shee's a whore." It was a fun show to do, demanding, Hume and Zobel were brilliant, and the audiences literally cheered for the characters they liked.

In the Fourth Spot was the new play for that year, Otis Bigelow's THE PREVALENCE OF MRS. SEAL. Otis gave it to us for no royalties as long as he could direct it. We hesitated, gave it to him, and he was a good director. Very good. And it was a successful comedy.

Somewhere in there was Brigid's puppet show, for children. QUALITY STREET closed the season. I may in fact have been in it, but don't remember.

We added some new people that year. Bob Wright was new, our only black actor. Also young, semi-Studly Ken Weisbarth, miserably miscast as the Rambler who steals Madge away in PICNIC, and the musician Joseph Lyons, who orchestrated some of our shows. Brigid Brine, our puppeteer was new. She did children's shows, which I not only did not see, I didn't care about them, either. More fool me.

It is interesting to note our 1977 Season Ticket prices: Six plays for 12 dollars. Which included Brigid's show.

The Season. It was interesting.

I think I got it right.

RIVER VALLEY CHRONICLE, Hudson, New York. October, 1977

The River Valley enjoyed a summer crowded with superb cultural events. Tanglewood, Lake George Opera, Mac-Haydn, all had glorious seasons with record attendance.

The joy of the Summer Season, however, was Lexington Conservatory Theatre . . .

'Tis Pity She's A Whore proved to be a stunning coup du theatre. Reaching back 400 years to produce John Ford's numbing tragedy of incestuous love was a risk that paid off in terms of Box Office and the satisfaction of high art . . . under the inspired direction of Oakley Hall III it was a miracle of life and spirit. The complexity of action, plot and subplot was carried forward wonderfully under Mr. Hall's unfailing eye.

The other risky production of Lexington Season 77 was the world premier of Otis Bigelow's play, *The Prevalence of Mrs. Seal*, which was a triumph of Box Office and art. If this marvelous Bigelow play doesn't soon arrive on Broadway then the theatre is in worse shape than many claim . . . Bigelow's deft mixture of humor and the bizarre has an ever present underpinning of the eternal problem man faces in handling the "gift of Life."

Quality Street, J.M Barrie's Classic comedy was Lexington's final production. It was all beauty, sentiment, and high style under Michael van Landingham's direction.

Talent, dedication, and hard work were the ingredients of Lexington Theatre's achievement. Sets and costumes were highly imaginative, a triumph of limitation of means. The company could boast a resident composer in Joseph Lyons. His original music for *'Tis Pity, Mrs. Seal*, and *Quality Street* added a unique effectiveness to those productions. The acting of the entire company was on an exceptionally high plane of excellence.

River Valley audience response this season shows their approval of reaching back 400 years for a play like *'Tis Pity*, discovering a brilliant contemporary work like *Mrs. Seal* and enjoying a 20th Century Classic like *Quality Street*. Their response clearly shows too their aversion to the cheap "Cotton Candy" productions that often pass as art works along the Summer Theatre Trail.

But we had occasional arguments, me and Vano, and occasionally Thomas Culp, now treasurer for LCT. We both liked Steven Patterson's direction of TAVERN. I didn't like, at all, Herndon's direction of PICNIC, or his casting, either. Vano liked both. Ah, well. Culp felt 'TIS PITY was just too big for Summer Stock and should be replaced with something smaller, but in fact I was already thinking about doing Marlowe's THE TRAGICAL HISTORY OF DOCTOR FAUSTUS for our '78 season. 'TIS PITY may have been big, but we would get bigger. I loved Otis Bigelow's casting and direction of THE PREVALENCE OF MRS SEAL. Vano disagreed.

It's the kind of thing that goes on in a Theatre Company. No one agrees on anything. No problem.

And we were starting to get reviews, and good ones, in papers like the River Valley Chronicle, the Woodstock Times, the Windham Journal, the Catskill Daily Mail.

Not, I'll admit, very Big Papers, but interesting. If we had set up our Lexington Conservatory Theatre so that we'd get reviews in bigger and bigger places, this would have been satisfying.

During the run of UBU We (UBU) met a man named Oscar Metenier. He came to the second night of UBU ROI and rather enjoyed it. Metenier had an Interest in the Theatre.

A kind of Obsession.

Metenier was a Policeman. And what he did was to accompany the condemned Men, or Women, to their deaths. And what he liked was that suspense, the Waiting, and then the Vision of the Person Dying.

The Head severed by the Guillotine. The Burst of Blood.

It was — almost — Disgusting to hear him talk.

Metenier talked to us about making UBU — well — Realer, making him work out some of His internal hatreds. We said We'd see.

Metenier was what was called a Naturalist.

We were what was known as an Illusionist. Soon, but long after we were dead, as a Surrealist.

One deals with Reality, as everyone understands it. The other deals with a Reality I make up.

Very, very different.

This is a curious contact. UBU ROI is sometimes called the Progenitor of GRAND GUIGOL. It isn't. At all. The attitudes are very different. UBU was basically skewed fun. Grand Guignol is an attack on Everything.

But it's fascinating to know that Alfred Jarry actually met Metenier. And what happened.

About six months later we got an Invitation from Metenier to go to the First Show in his Theatre, which was over by Montmartre.

The THEATRE DU GRAND GUIGNOL.

We walked to 20 rue Chaptal, in Pigalle. We arrived at the THEATRE DU GRAND GUIGNOL with Mme Rachilde and Toulouse-Lautrec, ready for anything. Fuelled with Absinthe.

The THEATRE DU GRAND GUIGNOL was in a building that used to be a Monastery, at the back of an alley.

A sign said GRAND GUIGNOL, in Red.

Then you were in a Chapel, and that was the Theatre.

There we were, Small, Large-hatted, with Mme Rachilde, as in-tox-i-ca-ted as We were, and with Toulouse-Lautrec. Going out with Toulouse-Lautrec was like walking a large, mismade dog, who tired easily.

Toulouse-Lautrec knew everybody. He knew Fermin Gemier, knew Lugne-Poe, knew Oscar Metenier, too.

We looked around, aware of how We looked: Tall-hatted, Smoking, accompanied by Mme Rachilde, whose Jewelry was not clanking. She had taken the fact that we were in the Pigalle seriously, and was dressed as a Semi-rich Peasant. This meant no Jewelry, and the Front of her Dress was made of Cardboard. Also she was not Acting, she was Baffled.

The Space was divided up the way one would a Chapel: the Stage being where the Archbishop used to stand. No Décor at all.

"Strange Theatre," said Mme Rachilde.

"It is," We said, "A making Holy of what was once Moral Suicide."

Lights. We knew a fair amount about them, having used them in Puppet-work, and at the Theatre when UBU was done. At Grand Guignol, they were Powerful Flames, well Controlled, and Acetylene, for Impact.

Behind the stage there were these Theatre-boxes, Seating boxes, covered with mesh; so one could see out, but not see in very well.

We knew what they were. Where one went for More-than-Solitary Pleasure.

We nodded, Ubiquely, toward the boxes.

Mme Rachilde looked at them, looked at us, and giggled. She knew, too.

"Ah, Monsieur Jarry," said a deep voice, and there was Metenier, dressed very neatly in a Suit. He shook our hand. We were impressed that he probably looked as neat that day as he did when he Took Condemned People to Death.

"M. Metenier. We are Us, this is Mme Rachilde, and Toulouse-Lautrec is somewhere."

Metenier said, "Charmed."

We said, "Metenier, this is a bizarre theatrical space."

Metenier said, "Ah —"

"We approve," We said, cutting off his response.

We looked around the space, Ubique, approving. Despite the fact that they were in Pigalle, a not-so-trendy area, the Audience was pretty organized, pretty well-dressed. There was a Bar where they were serving alcoholic beverages. We went to the bar and ordered "Two Absinthes."

We were sure Mme Rachilde wanted one, too.

Everything was new. New goblets, new sugar-holders. At least the Absinthe looked old: Green, Grainy, Poison Lurking. We got set to pay, but the barkeep said, "On Oscar."

There was a moment of Ubique confusion, and then We remembered that Metenier's name was Oscar Metenier.

We turned toward Metenier, and saluted him with Our Cup.

We held two fingers toward Mme Rachilde, as if holding a cigarette. She unloaded two, and We lit them at the sconces, holding real flames, that lighted the place.

"Strange — uh — scent," she said, exhaling smoke. Taking the Absinthe.

We sniffed. "It's wax. From when there used to be a Chapel here." We paused. "Maybe."

She looked alarmed. "It smells evil to me. Very evil."

"Ah, Cleo." This was in in-joke between us. She had written a novel in which Cleopatra was actually a Slender Boy.

"Evil." Another mouthful of smoke. Another jolt of Absinthe.

First Metenier spoke, briefly. He indicated that what we would see would be real. The Lights slammed out, Hummed a moment, and then slammed on again.

We were front row in the balcony, or at least Mme Rachilde and We were. We don't know what happened to Toulouse-Lautrec. We were slammed into an Apartment in Paris. There was a Woman there, other People Entered, there was a Terrifying Noise, the Woman was Raped and there was Blood everywhere. Blood! They must have used close to a Hundred Liters, in one, maybe ten-minute show.

It was terribly realistic.

It was also — almost — revolting.

"Evil," said Mme Rachilde.

"It is what They want to see," We said.

Also there were no Masks. None at all.

The lights came up, the Actors all bowed. It was curious that three of them were there at all, so Realistic were their Deaths.

We had a fair amount of time to get more Absinthe. Which We, for one, needed.

The second show was slower starting. But got much worse. And was only a one-act.

And there were people Doing the Dirty in the Backstage Boxes. We would have watched them, if we could have taken out eyes off the Gore-Circus in front of us.

We had another Absinthe, and spoke to Metenier.

"Maybe," We said. "We have to consider."

Metenier nodded.

"It's awesomely real," We said. "We don't know if We write that way."

"Oh, I think you do," said Metenier.

Really?

Metenier paid for all our Absinthes, which made me like him better.

*Blood. I think one of the reasons I selected 'TIS PITY SHE'S
A WHORE was that at the end of the show the Entire Cast is killed,
with daggers and knives and swords. A Lot of Blood. I think we used
Six Gallons of Blood a night. I invented a character,
LIMPIASANGRE, whose job it was to mop up the blood. As we
were making up the blood recipe there was a lot of discussion about
the color that Black Cherry versus Strawberry Jello gave to the mix.
And as I recall it was Kristin Joliff who discovered, after I began to
add Peanut Butter for texture, that several big spoonfuls of
Blackberry Jam gave it just the right luster. I loved her for that.*

I was haunted by GRAND GUIGNOL. It was almost as
if it were invented by UBU.

It was the Visual Aspect of it that kept me interested.
The Bright Lights, the Immense Shadows, the Loud
Screeching, the Bloodbath following. It was the Peril Coming,
that actually comes, that obsessed me.

And the Acetylene lights, Sheer Lighting power.

*Like Jarry, I was haunted by Grand Guignol. For him it was
being invented right in front of him. For me it was an Ancient Form,
containing much Odd Stuff. But fascinating in its ability to make
Horror Visible.*

Oscar Metenier kept asking to see my more Bizarre
Writings. I — We — wrote some stuff for him. We used a
Pseudonym.

We didn't think the work was very good, although
Oscar did.

It was not based on UBU ROI.

In 1889 Metenier disappeared. Literally. Didn't show up and work one day, and was simply Gone. No Suspicions, No one allegedly knew Anything. He was replaced as director of GRAND GUIGNOL by a fellow named Max Morey.

Morey was even more gory. If that's possible.

In New York City I went to anything that seemed Grand Guignol. There was a fair amount of it.

The titles of Grand Guignol plays are indicative: Anything with "Old Man" in the title has the ring of Grand Guignol. That was why I named my play about the Cenci family, part of the 78 Season, BEATRICE (CENCI) AND THE OLD MAN.

I may have started behaving strangely, too.

I may have started acting strangely around women. I may have started talking gutturally. I may have had hallucinations of Big People, not friendly, or strange, like Ubu, but menacing, and Big.

I may have.

After my death, Antonin Artaud, who ran the THEATRE ALFRED JARRY, invented the THEATRE OF CRUELTY. It's interesting to have a Theatre named after One, and really interesting to have a man like Artaud run it. Theatre of Cruelty is not Me, is not Mine.

I heard that Artaud Died on Stage, playing the Old Man in his play, THE CENCI. Interesting story. I hope it's true.

I find this curious: I wrote a play, called BEATRICE (CENCI) AND THE OLD MAN, not knowing that Artaud, author of THE CENCI, had been director of THEATRE ALFRED JARRY.

I had read Artaud's THE CENCI and it struck me as very imaginative. Then I read that it was based on Reality. Apparently there was, in the Sixteenth Century, a Merchant like Cenci, who was so Rich that he Bought Two Popes.

Bought Them.

So Rich that he couldn't be Prosecuted, even though everybody knew that he had Made Love to his Daughter Beatrice, who had a child by him, and then Cenci Slept with his own Granddaughter.

Of course it was a long time ago.

I made it more modern.

THE SETTING: The STORY is framed by the TRIAL. We need to be able to go from one to the other without breaks or changes of setting.

THE TIME: Now, though a slightly antique feel may be desirable.

ONE: 1: AT RISE: Empty courtroom. In the area approximating the audience section, LUCY and THEODORE. Enter ORSON, carrying a briefcase and several large books

with paper markers in
them. He puts these
on a table.

LUCY

O, Theodore, there's Orson. Orson!

ORSON approaches
them.

ORSON

Good morning, Mrs. C. Good morning Theodore.

THEODORE

May you rot.

*It's a Play, a Subject, that aims right for the Jugular. A
daughter, a Father, and the Daughter's Duty to do what her Father
says to do, even if it is Immoral.*
And her Heart tells her that She Can't.

LUCY
How does it look, Orson? Have you seen
Beatrice?

ORSON
Judge Pappas isn't making this easy for us. I
haven't been able to see Beatrice even once.

*And then She faces a legal system, run by a Father of the
Country. Dies; goes to Heaven, which is run by, you guessed it, God
the Father. All Fathers played by one actor.*

OLD MAN

Good morning. I would like to say a few words
before we begin. I am Judge Pappas, and this
is my court. If everyone will remember that,
and behave accordingly, there will be no
unpleasantness. I run an informal court, but
there are certain things I will not tolerate:
I will not tolerate outbursts of any kind. I
will not tolerate histrionics on the part of
the Defense Counsel, nor the constant cries of
"Your Honor, I Object!" that so impede the
course of Justice in our day. I will not
tolerate statements disrespectful or abusive
of the court, the legal Process, or the
Prosecution. If we all understand each other,
everything should go along swimmingly, and
Justice will be done.

It's a Surreal play, with a combination of seamy, turn-of-the-century Frankenstein-weird and Superreal Talk. And it's a combination Comedy and Tragedy.

Very Ubique, some might say.

Some fairly stylish writers hooked up with Oscar
Metenier's GRAND GUIGNOL.

We wrote Metenier a piece. It was all right, but Gory.

Everything there is Gory. Gory and Evil.

We made it very Sexy, too.

And all Masked. Everyone.

And We changed our Name.

We took Toulouse-Lautrec and went again. Grand
Guignol improves with seeing it several times. We also
studied the Back-stage Boxes, for interest in Who is doing
What to Whom.

That was intriguing.

I was not getting a lot of sleep during this period. In fact, I never got a lot of sleep. My hair had grown to my shoulders, and I wore a Top Hat, Women's Blouses, and Bicycle Shoes.

I was, in fact, going through my inheritance with some speed. So, needless to say, I started a magazine, L'YMAGIER, with Remy de Gourmont as co-editor. Devoted to Art, my definition of it, mainly religious, with Albrecht Durer engravings, and My Own woodcuts. I was, you know, a good artist.

Actually, I still am.

It was quite a beautiful magazine and we put out seven issues of it. Then I broke with Remy and put out PERHINDERION on my own; another beautiful magazine, with hand-set engravings by Durer, etc. My Drawings and Etchings. It was quite lovely, quite expensive, and did not pay back its owner (me) in any way, and exhausted my small fortune in only two issues. This was sad.

But intentional.

It was not my intention to make inroads into the Art community with money from My Parents. Not my intention at all. So I spent it.

The only problem was, Absinthe had an addictive quality to it. One can talk one's way around Addiction, and I did, but there it was.

I remember crossing the Bridge to the Lexington Bar and Grill — except there wasn't a Grill, only a Bar — to the one street in Lexington, turning Left, turning Left again, walking through a double-door, and then a single door, and there was the long bar, with

*the Tavern-Keeper, an elderly, bearded Russian, waiting. Waiting, it
seemed, for Me.*

*If I was in a good mood, Beer. If I was in a gnarly mood,
Bourbon.*

I went for a bicycle-wagon ride one day. I (Jarry) and
Mme Rachilde. She was in a wagon attached to the back of the
bicycle. I, Jarry, dressed for bicycling, was on the bicycle.

I always dressed up for bicycling, with Vallette or
Mme Rachilde. It was kind of like my boating costume, but not
quite.

Picture me, if you would, if you haven't already, as
small, physically fit, and dressed for whatever was going to
happen. With a very good bicycle.

We were at the top of a hill. I said, "We will go fast,
hang on, and you will be all right." We got going fast and after
a while Mme Rachilde complained that we were going too
fast. I said, "Mme Rachilde, your cart is pushing us now."

I got out my knife, tried to cut the ropes, and ended up
swinging off the bicycle and being dragged behind the cart to
slow us down.

Mme Rachilde was very grateful.

"Madame," I said, laconically, "We believe we were a
little frightened. And never have we wanted so desperately to
take leave of a Woman."

This is usually told as an example of my nature: half
noble, half criminal. Actually, it was a simple statement of
facts.

In Elizabethan texts, the plays, a Comic Moment
follows a Tragic one.

Comic works better after Tragic.

Elizabethan Fact. Also true.

Merdre.

And that is, in a sense, why I've written this Autobiography the way I have.

Except the problem with My Life is there is not Tragedy in it.

Or maybe it's a different kind of Tragedy.

L.C.T. might have been a Comedy. Comedy has central characters who collapse. In fact, that may be the central reason for Comedy to exist. For characters to collapse.

This could be said to be true of tragedy; thereby proving my point: Comedy and Tragedy are the Same.

Speaking of tragedy: Before Theatre de l'Oeuvre produced UBU ROI it produced Oscar Wilde's SALOME, starring Sarah Bernhardt as Salome. It was written in French, by an English playwright, the absolute master of Farce.

But SALOME was no Farce. It was an Epic Tragedy.

I met Wilde. He was Big. Tall and getting obese and Studiedly Homosexual. He also spoke French quite well.

"How charming to meet you, Mr. Jarry." Wilde took a long look at me. His eyes almost violet, and warm. I understood that Wilde had Charm. And Soft eyes.

"I loved SALOME," I confessed, "It was . . . haunting."

"Many thanks." He took a long drink.

I had some impression of trying to interest Wilde in my own Dramas, but He was Tragic in his attempts to be known as a Playwright, not a Farceur.

It appears the reason that he wrote so much was that he was trying to support Lord Alfred Douglas. A Homosexual affair, which later landed Wilde in Prison, for Two Years.

Ah, Merdre.

I got Ken Weisbarth to agree to paint the Barn Theatre in exchange for casting him in a Speaking Role in 'TIS PITY SHE'S A WHORE. I cast him in the part, which he did all right, and it took him almost ten weeks to paint the Barn.

It's a Big Theatre, but not that big.

I gave him a fairly hard time about the Time he was taking.

I was, allegedly, the only Carpenter. And carpentry took time, of which I didn't have much.

It was amazing that we got as much done as a group as we did, and amazing that we were so, allegedly, friendly.

1895, 19th of August: my father died. My sister Charlotte went South to work things out, and I went with her.

My own father has since died, but was still none of the things that I listed here.

It was curious: the "Plot" of BEATRICE (CENCI) AND THE OLD MAN is the same "Plot" that had 'TIS PITY SHE'S A WHORE removed from the British stage for 260 years.

Incest.

Now No One seemed to Understand that Incest was the subject in 'TIS PITY, but it's the whole point of BEATRICE (CENCI). They don't miss that, but it might be buried in the fact that BEATRICE (CENCI) is Funny.

Supposed to be Funny.

ONE: 2: Morning light. THEODORE, still chained, meditating. ENTER BEATRICE. SHE makes as if to rouse him, then doesn't, and waits. ENTER, from OLD MAN's room, LUCY. SHE is upset.

LUCY

Beatrice, where is your father?

BEATRICE shrugs.

THEODORE

In the "studio."

BEATRICE

I thought you were meditating.

THEODORE

I am. My astral body is in the studio with Daddy.

LUCY

What's he doing?

THEODORE

You don't want to know.

LUCY

Don't lie, Theodore. Your astral body is right here with us. You can't see anything. Your eyes are closed.

THEODORE

I can see the Studio. There are two people in
it: an older man and a young female. She is
tied up: her elbows are behind her back so
that her firm and ripe young--

LUCY

Now, Theodore, you just stop that!

"A bizarre Comedy," the posters read.

I saw my sister occasionally. And Henri Morin. He
visited me at times. He didn't see UBU ROI as a Stage Show,
for which I am glad.

Toulouse-Lautrec called us UBAH, and the mad
musician Satie called us BOO. Mme Rachilde called us UB.

*Zobel started calling me "the Alf," or "Ubu." This was
probably because I had a three-part moustache. Zobel couldn't grow
one. Nobody else tried.*

Erik Satie was not an Absintheur but a Calvadan, he
drank Calvados, and had probably the fastest hands I had ever
seen. He played Piano, at this point, other people's music,
until quitting time, when he switched over to his own work.

That's when we went, Quitting Time.

Two in the morning. After a while, because there were
a fair amount of us there, they moved quitting time to
Midnight.

Satie played brilliantly, through massive alcohol. And called us Boo.

My good friend Vallette at the *Mercure de France* bought and published DAYS AND NIGHTS.

Then we rented the 2-½th floor. 7 Rue Cassette.

Despite its very low ceilings, We rather liked the 2-½th floor. We, in fact, kept it till I allegedly died.

"Very low ceilings."

The floors of 7 Rue Cassette were divided horizontally and vertically. This made the rooms quite small, and the ceilings about five feet high.

It was perfect for Jarry. Caused anybody else bent heads.

Jarry, Courtly, Fully Extended. Everybody Else With Their Heads Bowed. The Short Man's Revenge.

I (Jarry) met with odd people in a Hotel, Rue Bara: Mme Rachilde, Vallette, Ravel, Remy de Gourmont, sometimes Picasso.

I was very neat, shook everybody's hand, and introduced Absinthe. There we had a fascinating meeting on Point of View.

We think it was Remy de Gourmont who said, "Point of View."

And We said, in our Ubique style, "Ah, well, Madame Rachilde does that very well."

Followed by a long silence.

And then Mme Rachilde, a Handsome, nay, incredibly beautiful woman, with the face of a child, her hair trimmed handsomely around it, her lower jaw thrust out, dressed in Very Expensive Peasant Clothing, shook her head and said, "Ah, yes, Point of View." And then started to tell us, in great detail, something that We, and We suspect all the others there, did not understand a bit.

And she did know Point of View. And she looked so perfect there, her jangly silver bracelet up her arm, her shoulders moving beneath her Peasant blouse, and how she said, "Right, M. Jarry?"

I was getting all the usual bullshit. Best Artistic Director since American Conservatory Theatre's Bill Ball, etc. I know it as bullshit now, but then I thought it was due me as a hard-working, hard-drinking Man of the People.

William Ball lost his theatre and died, committed suicide, in Los Angeles.

Ah, well. Lexington was a good place for me, for a while.

There was another production of UBU ROI, this time using Marionettes, done by Pierre Bonnard's Troupe, Theatre Des Pantins. This was more satisfying than the first production, by a lot. It was more controlled by Us. It was better.

It was much better.

I gave them many ideas about UBU's stance, MOTHER UBU's flirting, MACTURDY's chest-out posturing. It was successful.

I was dressed Ubique and acted like UBU too.

So I was We.

They built all the puppets for UBU excepting UBU, which was Ours. We, that is Jarry, built it. And that's the way it ought to be.

Jarry never saw UBU as anything but a Puppet. So having real actors play UBU was a built-in Dead Loss, for Jarry. He had a Directorial Style, and what he loved about Actors, was their Ability to Play Nothing when they were Not On Stage. That, perhaps, and, perhaps the Absinthe.

I had another book, a Conception, called L'AMOUR EN VISITES, which Vallette wouldn't publish, but Mme Rachilde got me a publisher for it.

In fact it was Paul Fort.

Who was now, after Artistic Directing the Theatre d'Art, publishing Pornography.

Far from being Pornography, the Novel is a Confession that I am Homosexual.

Which I, then, was.

Paul Fort wrote his usual one-third educated letter, promising me wads of money for a novel called L'AMOUR EN VISITES. He didn't read the novel; he approved it by looking at a list of Chapter Headings.

There's a chapter called VISITING THE OLD LADY, that is word-for-word quotes from letters I'd received from Berthe de Courriere, my ex-Friend's Mistress.

I thought this, the Writing, might be fun.

It turned out to be Wrong.

I had written fiction before and always easily.
L'AMOUR EN VISITES was hard, sometimes very hard.
Especially the VISITING THE OLD LADY sequence. Most of
which I stole.

From the Reality.

*Stealing from Reality. I stole much of MIKE FINK's size
from thinking about Big Dick, the Man who Lived Across the Road
in Squaw. And some of that same Size-thinking went into
Frankenstein's Monster, combined with my thoughts on the subject
of Deformity and Dreams on that Subject after I had my Facial
Accident with the Stone Bench at Andover.*

*All the FRANKENSTEIN scenes with his FATHER were
parodies of scenes I felt could have happened with my Father. Ditto
the whole concept of BEATRICE (CENCI) AND THE OLD MAN.
Not that anything like Incest went on in my house, but the whole
concept of Paternal Authority. Twisted.*

I happen to think all writers work this way.

They wanted to send us to Prison. The Prison of
Health. We didn't want to be a Prisoner there.

At all.

*Ah, yes, Health. The curious thing about Health is,
everybody who was Healthy in the Theatre is dead by the age of 50.*

Or, like Jarry, even earlier.

*But then, Jarry was never Healthy. Not ever. The constant
mention of his Racking Cough, his Nerves; and bear in mind that*

Jarry's Mother's Mother and Brother were confined for Insanity, several times.

Which Jarry knew.

Vallette and I exercised together in the mornings. I invested so much in allegedly destroying myself, and worked very hard on my health. That was it. It was mine, my health, and it was Us: UB.

We would take off our UBU costume — we had slept in it — and put on our Jarry costume.

We would shave, with the Throat-cutter Sir Alfred had given us.

Brush our teeth, with a stick of wood.

Make urine in a small bowl, and then "Gardez-Loup," throw it out the window.

Then I would bicycle — on Jarry's very, very good bicycle — or boat, or fence, or fish. I would exchange words on Literature of some kind or other, with Vallette, who then went to work at the *Mercure*, and I went to write, or, more often later, to Absorb the Sense of Absinthe that clung around places like Le Rat Mort.

But we were writing. All the time, Writing. It was a disease I picked up when I was Human. Now of course we are UB.

Right. One must not forget. UB.

Once you write, and believe in what you do, it is almost impossible to stop.

I have discovered this since the Accident.

Ubu is bestial, almost non-human, not a great thinker. Useful, though, to construct one, if one doesn't have one's own mind, all the way.

It's as if Jarry, in creating and becoming Ub, was trying to flee from his own, too-analytical spirit.

Too analytical.

In a way it was the same for me. Translating, directing, even acting in UBU REX was a retreat from the irritations of being Artistic Director.

And Ubu became important to me in other ways. Later.

Pa Ubu, lithographed by Jarry for the cover of the musical score by Claude Terrasse, "Ouverture d'Ubu Roi, pour piano à 4 mains," 1898.

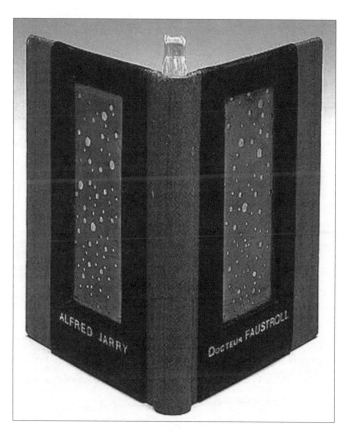

Like many artists who are only posthumously celebrated as geniuses, Jarry never saw his work widely appreciated. This leather-bound volume of his *Dr. Faustroll* appeared in 1923, sixteen years after his death.

We started wearing a very Big, very off-White coat, with Black Marks above the Pockets. And a Boule-dogue in each Pocket.

Boule-dogues are Pistols. Which We Kept Loaded. In case Attacked. We were tried several times in court for attacks upon people with our Boule-dogues, but acquitted every time.

One Judge dismissed the case because a Midget has a right to carry Boule-dogues and use them if Crowded.

This incensed Us.

WE ARE NOT A MIDGET. WE ARE UBU. KING OF POLAND.

We slicked back our shoulder-length Hair, and blackened our own Caporal. We had sleepy eyes, and did not have to imitate anybody for Our Voice was already Ubique. We said "Merdre" when we arrived at Le Rat Mort, or the Chat Noir, each morning, and everybody said "Merdre" also. We had them trained so that they would already have Absinthe Sweetening, in front of UBU's chair. We would roll Ourself up a cigarette of that American drug, Tobacco, and smoke it as we drank.

And We wrote well this way.

We started in upon THE GESTURES AND OPINIONS OF DOCTOR FAUSTROLL, 'PATAPHYSICIAN. And finished it. In Le Rat Mort.

There, and at Rousseau's, where we moved when we were evicted from the Blvd Port Royale.

DOCTOR FAUSTROLL: Our "Neo-Scientific Romance." We thought it would not be published until We got to someplace where We could appreciate it.

That is to say, when We Were Dead.

I felt similarly about Lexington Conservatory Theatre.

That no one would understand it 'til I was Dead.

That no one would, for example, understand the almost-sexual attempts to make FRANKENSTEIN up from scratch, the distinctly Sexual attempts to make Winship Cook play a Very Sensual Old Woman in 'TIS PITY. And would they understand the importance of Richard Zobel's UBU? His lack of control and hypercontrol?

They wouldn't understand it 'til I was Dead.

But unlike Jarry, I put that a long way into the future.

We got Our Absinthe with My Boule-dogues.

We suspect this was not quite real, but a charming face put on the fact that the Owner, of, say the Dead Rat, was trying to support Us, without showing it.

We are UBU, and UBU's real because he is Us. He is the necessary transfiguration of a Poor Playwright, an unsold Novelist, a maker of Things with no Theatre to use them. UBU's the symbol of everything unused in the world. It's all UBU.

And UBU is Us.

We knew, in our Jarry-head, that Absinthe was killing us. But to our UBU-head, it didn't matter.

At all.

There was an I/We split in me too.

We were considered Charming, by the owners of the Taverns.

Charming. I grew accustomed to it, and Ubu was Ub.

As LCT developed there was an I – and there was a We. I am told that I did things: like lecturing the Bar-crowd at the Bar across the River on FRANKENSTEIN. Like quite verbally hating PICNIC. Which we did. Horribly Miscast.

That wasn't Me. That was Us.

Drunk. Or: And Drunk.

Lord Alfred Douglas came back to Paris. He spoke French rather badly and I, despite my translations from the English (THE RIME OF THE ANCIENT MARINER) spoke English worse. But I understood him. He said Oscar was in Prison.

Because of Lord Alfred's father's doings.

Note: Alfred Douglas's father pursued Oscar into a jail term that ended his Drama-writing career, without ever mentioning that his own son, Alfred, was Wilde's semi-permanent lover.

Lord Alfred Douglas looked like a very autocratic child, which is what he was. He was also an Absintheur. His face was long, noble, hair slicked back. We drank together. I drank with a man who lived with Oscar Wilde, certainly the greatest comic mind of the century. As Wilde was in prison, in

England, Lord Alfred Douglas traveled with his group of "Boys," as he called them. They would Stage Plays.

Sometimes I took part.

Wilde was in prison, serving time for Homosexuality, but his Lover was cruising. He and his "Friends" all used Wilde canes: very long, and heavy.

They restaged Wilde's SALOME, with a Homosexual cast. I took the part of Director, ordering "boys" here, Lord Alfred Douglas there, Myself here, there, everywhere.

Lord Alfred Douglas said "O, it was written with this stuff in mind, you know. Oscar Wilde was Queer."

Actually, Oscar Wilde was still alive. And Lord Alfred Douglas was "Queer."

I was told, by Lord Alfred, that I was a pretty good Director.

Also I heard that I was "Well-hung."

This somehow pleased me, or pleased the UBU in me.

I began to have hallucinations.

We are haunted by Death.

UBU is not dying. We are UBU.

And UBU is Us.

Not the UBU that I made. Another UBU. A god, of sorts.

As Lord Alfred says, "A God. A deity. A weird God, who makes us comfortable, and then breaks into strange behavior, Is Sexual. Is Dirty."

Is, in fact, Ubique.

Though We don't think, necessarily, that UB is a homosexual.

But He might be.

But We don't think so. UBU is Simple. Straightforward. And Stupid.

Not Homosexual, which takes some Intelligence.

We think.

I am not Gay, but happen to believe this, too.

We are KING UBU. We have MOTHER UBU.

We are trying to go one step further, by becoming Dr. Faustroll.

It is one step further because Dr. Faustroll was sixty-three years old when he was born in 1898. The Twentieth Century was then − 2 years old.

And he (Dr. Faustroll) maintained this age all his life.

So he didn't get any older.

Or younger.

This is nice.

But we might not make it.

The Not-getting-older part.

UBU. Us.

After Hébert. Eb. Ebon. Ebance. Ebouille. P.H. Ub. UBU.

We were UBU. This is not simply a case of a Playwright taking a Main Character who was wildly successful and milking it. Oh no.

This is a lot Deeper. We never thought about M. Hébert any more. It was UBU, and the UBIQUE world. To Everything there was the UBU way of responding.

And Absinthe made it all so clear.

UBU.

And Hallucinatory.

I wrote many plays, they could be called THE HALLUCINATIONS OF UBU.

I threw them all away.

It is not UBIQUE to have hallucinations.

Except the whole Ubique Cycle is Hallucinatory.

I began, that winter between the 77 and 78 seasons, to have what I call my Ubique Hallucinations. They were Ubique in terms of what I Saw, but there was none of Jarry's humor.

I saw Big Men, and Big Women, too. This was partly due to the fact that I went to a big Gay bar on the Lower West Side. To Look and See, not to Do. They were There, and began to haunt my Dreams as well. Big People, Big Nostrils, flaring, and leaking some Clear Fluid. Big Breasts, both Male and Female. Big People taking Little People under their Wings.

And the Menace, always There. The shouting Matches. The Hissy Fits, the Menace Waiting in the Background.

Waiting.

I notice, when sitting on the two feet over the hole, that Absinthe tightens my bowels. All my life my bowels have been very loose.

With Absinthe, they get tighter.

My brain, too, is tighter. More Beyond-Real, perhaps, but Tighter, more Organized.

The interesting thing is, I, Oakley Hall III, have all my life had loose bowels. Working on this Autobiography made them tighter. More Beyond-Real, but Tighter.

My brain? It got looser because of the Accident. It may be getting Tighter now.

We had a slight disagreement with Our Landlord. On the subject of Rent. Which We did not have.

Merdre.

So We moved. Again.

To the "Apartment" of Le Douanier Rousseau.

Where We Simply Arrived.

And We were haunted by Jarry's racking cough. Though We were UBU.

Jarry's cough has always bothered Us. Not quite Right, as others say — not Us, not UBU.

But UBU moved in, Spectacularly, on the Douanier Rousseau. He was a friend. We recommended his Art to people, occasionally. We didn't like it much Ourself, but We recommended it.

Avenue du Maine, I remember, We remember. Was where he lived. Had to change Our route, slightly, to go to Le Rat Mort.

The Dead Rat remained the same: Lesbic.

But now that I was becoming "Well-known" in certain circles, it was a little hard to pursue my "Little Boy" attitude. If I did not have Mme Rachilde with me, the women were quite odd.

But the Women were . . . One in particular. Jeanne. Short. Breasts Strapped Down. Short haircut, a Hand-Rolled always in her mouth. She took to calling me Hoob. And suggesting that I do strange things with her. I Ubu'd it, but it was unnerving.

These women were the same sex as my Mother.

This upset me.

In my sleep Jeanne would appear, Bigger, more Intense. "Hoob," She would Hiss, "Are you a Real Man? Or some Playwright's sense of what Real Men Are? Hey?"

Then she would approach closer: "A Real Man? or a Dream?"

Her Nostrils would Flare, Greasy. She would take off her Shirt, revealing Breasts, Very Large, attached to Leather by Bolts, and pulled Down, Bleeding Slightly.

They, the Breasts, would get bigger. She came Closer.

I had similar Dreams, and Hallucinations, and they ended Worse.

In Paris people knew us as UBU and would shout things. You know, "Hey, UBU! Are you Drunk?"

We said, "Oui-ah." Although we weren't drunk.

Absinthe, yes. Alcohol, no.

There is a difference between Them. If they point to Jarry as a man who was always drunk, that is not true.

Always Absinthed, yes.

Until the last two years of his, Jarry's, life.

When the drug of choice became Ether.

Which has nothing to recommend it. I have taken it, and it reduces all Life to a Giggle. Not the Giggle-thinking, just the actual Giggle. I found it irritating, as did Jarry. But it was a lot cheaper. He'd made a friend at the Hôpital de Charité who gave it to him.

Mme Rachilde (ferociously successful) and Vallette rented a place at 19 quai de l'Apport, and wanted some people to go in with them. We (UBU) did.

We called it "le Phalanstere." We worked there on DOCTOR FAUSTROLL. It was 1898.

L'AMOUR EN VISITES was published.

I was not proud, except that I, Jarry, did something without Ubu knowing about it. So We (UBU) doesn't know what I (Jarry) did.

Ha-ha.

Note (in case you haven't): The Ubu/Jarry connection is breaking down.

We is UBU; I is Jarry. I used to control We, but doesn't anymore.

In fact, We might now control I − as Jarry gets a laugh out of "We not knowing what I did."

This seems like Literary-fake, but it's real.

As Jarry, there are certain things I do. I still exercise with Vallette.

As UBU, we ridicule these things. As if they are a part of something else, something Normal.

We are Not Normal. Paris is strange. It hovers, it looms, it is unpredictable. We do certain things at certain times. Drinking Absinthe. Writing from the point of view of Dr. Faustroll. Going to Mallarmé's Funeral. Writing LE GRAND PAN EST MORT, which was published. I was Jarry at the funeral, and Jarry wrote MORT. We are usually UBU. And sometimes, of late, We have been becoming Dr. Faustroll.

Note this well.

In a letter to Mme Rachilde We said that We had been examined by "Merdecins." The "Docturds." We are simply going to "go out," like a lamp, not explode. Then they examine Our little turdlets, and figure out Why. We were all prepped for Death: UBU had a mauve shirt, and had shaved, with Lord Alfred's cut-throat razor.

This all, however, proved to be premature.

I was having trouble coping with something, though I am not sure what it was. Maybe it was my wife Meg. I don't remember too much about that relationship, but something, somewhere, was wrong.

I have no idea what it was.

And I have thought about it for many years.

I started Drinking my Breakfast at the Bar across the River. And my Lunch. And my Dinner.

We had always thought that one could write Fiction easily and make tons of money — à la Rachilde. But Rachilde's husband, Vallette, wouldn't or couldn't help me anymore with Long Fiction.

He read and dismissed DR. FAUSTROLL. He couldn't, he said, publish it. He curled his long mustachios in his hand.

"Couldn't," he said.

We look like a Short Man in a Top Hat and UBU Costume, but we are More. We are the Inventor of Carpet Slippers.

We Absinthed here and there, We spoke like UBU, and had our little party of Ubiques: Mme Rachilde for one, Toulouse-Lautrec for another, Picasso.

I consumed a certain amount of Absinthe, rolled a cigarette, and I became We. We were not simply Ubu, it was M. Ubu. We had pistols, which we waved around. We ignored this Tiny Body of Jarry's and became BIG.

Our voice became louder. Our swear-words more Ubique. We became Ubu.

But Ubu doesn't drink Absinthe. We ordered cheap white wine. I, Jarry, ordered Absinthe. From which Ubu, and my becoming Ubu, comes.

The Green, The Green from which Ubu comes. The Sugar-watered Absinthe. The Bad Taste. Green.

End of January, 1899. Le Phalanstere taken back by the Landlord. Some grief.

I am a little uncertain why the landlord took it back. Might have had to do with the rent. Possibly even My rent.

"Merdre." I said.

Trying to pretend it was UBU.

It wasn't.

It is the case, I think, that Jarry uses his UBU-mutation as a device to cover Jarry's failure, or what Jarry thinks of as his failures. It's fun, but not particularly rewarding to the psychic soul that looks for the real Jarry/Ubu in his autobiography.

I did the same thing, though the other Me was Twisted.

19 of May. Saw and met Oscar Wilde again. He was with Lord Alfred. He looked exactly like the ex-convict he is — tall and bent, and he did not carry a Wilde-cane. It was disappointing.

I gave him my book of "pornography," L'AMOUR EN VISITES. He seemed Faintly Charmed. In fact everything about him is Faint.

And this is Oscar Wilde, a writer that turned English Theatre from remakes of ANTONY AND CLEOPATRA to wonderful English Comedies.

And there is nothing Funny about him.

In either sense of "Funny."

It is interesting that truly "Funny" people are almost never Funny in real life. The point here might be that Wilde is out of Prison, and isn't very Funny, but apparently he wasn't all that Funny before, either.

I once met Josh Mostel, who like his father Zero Mostel, seemed always to be analyzing. Trying to figure out what is funny about any scene that presents itself.

And life is made up of scenes.

"Veritable portrait de Monsieur Ubu,"
woodcut by Jarry for the first edition of *Ubu Roi*, 1896.

We may not impress Wilde very much, either.

He kind of avoids Us. And is nervous when We show up.

We are mildly Obsessed with Wilde. We don't know why. Possibly the finest comic in English literature, and We don't Like him, or even Respect him.

Age. Wilde is older than We are. And We feel Old. How must Wilde feel?

We asked him if he was going to do any more comedies.

He shook his head. "I don't think so," he said.

We asked him if he was going to pursue the direction of SALOME.

He looked, well, stung. "A great play, SALOME. Unappreciated. No, I don't think I'll do that, either."

Curious. The English Prisons have taken his Genius for comedy and made it — Old.

Old.

Followed, in most cases, by Dead.

We, the League of Theatre Artists and Lexington Conservatory Theatre, were Young. We never thought about Age. It wasn't Relevant. I was twenty-eight when the Accident occurred.

We were Young, and Active, doing way too much work for the amount of time we had.

We thought about Death quite a bit. Avant-garde as we were, our heroes were all dead. Jarry and Artaud. Those were mine.

Van Landingham, with his huge beard and semi-long hair, liked turn-of-the-century lighting maniacs. Hume, with his face eternally young, eternally happy, liked people, actors mostly, who were dying when my father was born.

But Jarry has a sense that Death is Waiting.

Started writing hard. Really hard. Published QUESTIONS OF THEATRE and ROMAN D'UN DESERTEUR, *Novel of a Deserter*. Don't get us wrong. We didn't feel we had deserted France, no. It was more complex than that. Read the book. He said, trying to boost sales of his book, even though he is dead.

We think.

QUESTIONS OF THEATRE were a lot of questions that came to mind during the staging of UBU ROI. Most of them don't make any sense, but it's amusing.

Bear this in mind: I don't like Theatre very much.

Late 1899. La Frette. Rented. Very little money. It was there that I wrote, or re-wrote, UBU ENCHAINED. I had Guillaume Appolinaire and Pablo Picasso over, and offered them Absinthe, which is, in fact, all I have.

Appolinaire: "No, merci."

Picasso: "Eh, oui."

Several times.

Picasso. The word is that he is trying to become Us. We don't see it, but —

We gave a party at the ex-stables I lived in, at the Coudray locks. I caught a fish for each person, and we had enough wine and Absinthe for a small army. Mme Rachilde, despairing of Our ability to eat, made a gigantic chocolate mousse, in a salad bowl, which when turned over, looked like — We said it: "This represents the Left Breast of the Giant Negress of the Carnival in the Place du Thorn. Mme Rachilde copied it from Life in chocolate and vanilla, using Mother Fontaine's milk, who, as the whole countryside knows, sleeps with her goat . . . ." the rest of the made-up testament was lost in applause. And that was good, because I was fading, or We were.

Picasso was there. He got a section of the Breast of the Giant, but took it away with him.

We're not sure we had too much to do with his becoming Picasso.

We think it is, in his case, inborn.

It is curious the way that Jarry has contact with people who are known. Wilde. Picasso. Toulouse-Lautrec.

Is it that Jarry is a Minor Figure at the Turn of the Century?

Or is it that Jarry did not live long enough to become a Major Figure?

Mme Rachilde is here, and Vallette, and Lord Alfred and Wilde, and Toulouse-Lautrec. Toulouse-Lautrec is a mocker, and mocks everything. Wilde is very close with Lord Alfred, very close, like a Woman.

Mme Rachilde seems distant, far away. Absinthe, maybe.

We, too, seem far away. From Ourself.

Have changed "here" to a ritzier place. The Rat Mort was a little — well — Lesbic.

UBU drinks at classier places, because Poland pays for it. Dr. Faustroll drinks at classier places because he's — well — Faustroll.

So now we go to the CHAT NOIR. They are classier, and have very funny comedy after it gets dark. We suck Absinthe and smoke cigarettes. We entertain Mme Rachilde, or Toulouse-Lautrec, or Lord Alfred.

These are my Artistic Director notes, from LCT's 1978 program, describing our new-play series, PROVOS. It is curious that in the previous programs, in 1976 and 1977, there are no notes from me, Artistic Director, although Vano, as Managing Director, always had some commentary for the audience to read.

But in 1978 I was compelled to write something about our PROVOS program. That year I translated UBU ENCHAINED, and we did a Reading of it. It worked pretty well but there was no sense that a production of it was Wanted.

By this time Provos had read and produced many new plays by new playwrights. Some of them even became Known. Some of the playwrights have Gone On to Fame.

PROVOS was born, to be precise, the same night that the Lexington Conservatory Theatre took on its unique personality. Mike Hume and I had been moving bed frames all day, trying to create a space that was later to become the notorious barn theatre. That evening we got together with Michael van Landingham over a few drinks and began to fantasize about some use to which those hundreds of bedframes could be put. We talked of cutting and welding them together to create a stage set, a set for a play so hostile that the set itself would attack the actors. By a natural progression we got to talking about FRANKENSTEIN. Hume had just been fired from his job in New York City because the cook in the restaurant had punched him out (figure it . . .) and looked grotesque; at that moment the idea of doing FRANKENSTEIN as a new adaptation from the novel was born. In that moment also lay the germ of PROVOS, for FRANKENSTEIN was never anything but a work-in-progress, a play that grew in direct proportion to the input of the performers and technicians.

In many ways FRANKENSTEIN was a nightmare. Ask anyone who worked on the show. But it had a quality of life, which came from everyone's sense that he or she was creating the scene in which he or she currently worked. It was electrifying. For me as a playwright it was revolutionary, for I came to realize that the dynamics of theatre do not happen on the page, but on the stage.

This year we have tried to systematize that experience, and make it available to a handful of playwrights: To offer them the opportunity to hear their words and see their actions on the stage . . . The basic thrust of PROVOS is to help playwrights to create the kind of play that will transform — hopefully for the better — the kind of theatre in which we work, and which can define our world.

Funny, I do not currently remember FRANKENSTEIN in any way as a "nightmare."

BEATRICE (CENCI) AND THE OLD MAN, now that was.

1899, Finished, after all these years, UBU ENCHAINED.

It's all right. Basically it's UBU ROI, backward.

UBU ROI, UBU CUCKOLDED, UBU ENCHAINED. I have three of them.

I publish some things.

Goodbye, 19th Century.

1901. Does it feel new to me, the New Century?

It ought to. Feel New. Feel the Rebirth Coming.

Feel the Ubique Changes, and later, the Faustrollian sense that nothing matters very much, nothing intrudes, when you are 63.

I would like to live to be 63, but I doubt it.

I must have been present at the rehearsal of BEATRICE (CENCI) AND THE OLD MAN, but I don't remember.

I was quite probably in-tox-i-ca-ted. I would probably shout things: "Sofia (Beatrice), more retiring!" or "Old Man (Rotblatt), you need to Glide more." Or "Soltanoff (Theodore, the Old Man's youngest son), more intense! Tenser!"

And bear in mind that Wendy Chapin was directing the Play.

This may have bothered me. Or the fact that Hume wouldn't play the Old Man. Rotblatt was fine as the Old Man, but something bothered me about the situation.

I was drunk. And messed up some other way, but I don't know what the other way was. Quite probably I was arrogant.

I don't remember.

We think about Death a good deal. Death is a friend of Ours, as it were. But what is Death? Yes, We know there are

Thousands of Popular Theories about Death, but We would like to know. Can We experience Death, and then return, to Write about it, drink Absinthe, while Talking about It?

Maybe.

Maybe not.

We believe that the Brain continues to function After Death, and its Dreams are our Paradise.

We wonder: can We Commit Suicide, and come back?

                    JUDGE PAPPAS

And may the Lord have mercy on your soul.

                    BEATRICE

I am afraid — that He won't. I slew a Father,
and am punished by another Father, who sends
me to the tender mercies of still another
Father, who art in Heaven. I am afraid that
God will be prejudiced against me because of
what I have done. And yet, where can I turn?
Life and Death and Everything seems all to be
an endless vista of Fathers, from which I
cannot escape even by dying. This I swear: I
will not kill my Father anymore. Unless I have
to.

                              JUDGE PAPPAS gives
                              the signal. BAILIFF
                              begins to pedal the
                              generator. BEATRICE
                              thrashes and goes
                              rigid. Fade to BLACK.

I thought about Death a lot, Not like it was going to happen to me, but I thought about it. Jarry was dead. Artaud was dead. Marlowe was dead.

I wondered what it was like, being Dead.

I had may people's versions of what it was like.

I am not sure I bought any of them.

When I Drank Cleaning Acid, in the Army, it was an attempt to Commit Suicide and come back after, But I failed to Commit Suicide.

Back in '65, when I dove from the Elevation on which sat the Campus Church at Andover onto a snow-covered Stone Bench, smashed my head, my face, they wrote it up as a Suicide Attempt. It wasn't. I just mistook the solid-concrete bench for a pile of snow, and was diving into it.

I bit the end of my tongue completely off and managed to walk from Church, about a mile to the Infirmary, before collapsing.

That was a sign of my Will to Live, which I, at Lexington, tested again.

1901. We made it to the New Century.

We are twenty-eight years old. We played Troll of the Court again in Lugne-Poe's attempt to re-stage PEER GYNT. It was vaguely haunting, not having the premiere of UBU ROI to follow it.

It worked for what it was. The Theatre de l'Oeuvre still exists, with money from PEER GYNT, and other things.

Not that we care very much.

Above: The Lexington Conservatory Theatre Company, circa 1977, shortly before the author's Accident.

Below: The author at about this time, after his fascination with Jarry had moved him to adopt the Caporal three-pointed moustache.

Photographers unknown.

I don't remember what I was thinking about, before the Accident. I was developing an attitude that Alcohol was good, was a part of Life in the Theatre. I may have had an attitude before that, that all of Lexington Conservatory Theatre was Mine, not Ours.

"That could be an error," said Bouchard. He had bummed a Camel off of me, and was smoking it in his way, with intensity.

Zobel was there, too. He was drinking Bourbon, and smoking a Camel, his own.

And Sofia Landon.

I had Bourbon with a beer back. Bouchard had vodka-and tonic. Sofia had a Coke.

"The people might come to see the Actors Acting, the Show," suggested Bouchard.

"Yeah, but it was due to my work that they have any place to appear."

"But if it weren't for them, for us, you wouldn't have done all this work. It seems to me," said Bouche, through the cigarette, "that you are setting up a Company-Oakley split, when it shouldn't be there." He put the cigarette in an ashtray, and drank some Vodka-tonic. "We are You, and You are Us, and that's it."

He looked at me in that way he has, the innocent child waiting to be hit, and raised his finger for another Vodka-tonic.

Zobel: "I'll have a Bourbon."

I looked at Bouchard, He at me, with his Camel in his mouth.

"So you don't think," I said, trying to make it all humorous, "That people come here to see Playwrights, the Designers and Clean-up Crews working out their small attacks?"

"No," he said, accepting with a wave his Vodka-tonic. "And the word is you're drinking too much."

Sofia: "That is the word. Too much." Don't forget, she was married to Van Landingham.

Zobel said, "I like the way Jarry died. Maybe you could pull that off, you know. Paralyzed from the waist down, go to Hospital, ask for a Toothpick. Die."

Sofia said: "Actually, there is the worry that you are going to die, spectacularly, but still, Dead. And that, in my opinion, would be Too Bad." She took a drink of her Coke. "Yeah, it'd be Cute, but there you are, Dead."

"Dead," said Bouchard.

"It's a nice tribute to Jarry," said Sofia. "But maybe too far to go."

We wonder if we can die, and come back, and describe things from Being Dead. We kind of wish We could do it, without actually Killing Ourself. But We can't think of any Other Way.

And We've thought about it quite a bit.

We've also thought about the fact that We are losing money. It's Expensive to be UBU in Paris.

Actually, We assume it's expensive to be UBU anywhere.

Now, if We Were UBU, We could Kill Ourself, and Come Back to Life, with tons of interesting, or not-so-interesting things to say about it.

But We Are UBU.

Aren't We?

There are other places like This, but This is the most obvious. We get the sense from these words, especially, "Aren't we?" that Jarry is losing track of Jarry. Not surprising, considering. Absinthe. Constant attention being paid to UBU.

And, possibly, Loneliness.

I experienced Loneliness, for example, at Lexington, when I came back. Being constantly introduced as "The man who wrote FRANKENSTEIN, that piece . . . "

And they had all seen FRANKENSTEIN.

Ah, UBU. More and more We find Ourself being Dr. Faustroll. UBU's life seems, well, Trapped. He can only Be what He Is. We can only Be what We Are. And it's amazing what a Trap King of Poland can be When you're so Stupid that you run the World.

The World.

A Trap.

I began to think that way too.

I had a — hallucination, which I shall relate. It's kind of Charming.

I am (hallucinating) at Le Rat Mort. The Bounceress is Jean who has no shirt on. There are Bolts through her Nipples and Leather Straps —

I have told you all this —

She is much Bigger too.

She Snarls at me, and Plucks her Leather Straps.

It's a strange one — the Hallucination.

But Absinthe doesn't work the way it used to. It no longer has the power to put everything in the UBIQUE world, instantly. Or we are so permanently Absinthiated that there is no change. Curious, and faintly alarming.

Everything is Faint, here. Wherever Here is. Nothing matters very much. It's all interesting to describe: the birds fighting over a crumb of bread, the four-in-the-morning erect-walk home, the fact that it gets colder in winter, much colder. But it isn't very interesting, no sense that the cold of winter could make a man freeze to Death. Not much Drama, as Lord Alfred would say.

There is Drama, but it's in Private Things: the possibility, ever-growing, that you messed up somewhere, that you've traded a once brilliant eye for an Absinthiated scowl. Like Erik Satie you've become a piano-player in a bar, drunk.

But Erik Satie killed alcohol as one of his followers.

Alfred Jarry hasn't killed Absinthe.

It's still a follower of his. And a Powerful one. It's Green, and Bitter, and an Absolute.

It affects Me in Strange Ways. I still Gardez-Loup Urine out the window. I haven't passed any Shit in about a year. I rise early, having gone to bed late, I menace my Face with the Cut-throat razor Lord Alfred gave me. But nothing grows there any more.

Three-part Moustache, and that's it.

I have become Myself. Ourself. Perfect.

I write every day, mostly Operettas, with Perfect Lyrics.

But I sense, or We sense, that no-one cares any more.

This is Life, for the UBIQUE followers. Perfect, and no-one cares.

Merdre.

```
TWO: 4 (Epilogue):
DUMBSHOW: The OLD MAN
is robed in white.
BEATRICE enters,
looking slightly ill-
at-ease, goes to him.
HE ignores her. SHE
goes to her knees,
her head down, HE
turns to her, raises
her up. THEY embrace.


NOTE: BEATRICE can
either play this
straight, or ironic.



        THE  END
```

I thought, as I wrote it, that BEATRICE (CENCI) AND THE OLD MAN was the Perfect Ubique Play.

And I'm fairly sure Wendy did not think it was Ubique at all.

But I don't remember.

I do remember that I wore a Bowler Hat. An indication of something, though I don't know what.

I'm also not sure I knew then, either. Bowler Hat means −.

Possibly it meant that I couldn't get a Top Hat.

As Jarry had.

I am pretty sure I messed with Wendy's direction of BEATRICE rehearsals. Pretty sure I talked too much.

I remember very little of the show, but what I do remember was Dark. Waiting.

Theodore Soltanoff as Theodore, chained to the stairs, whimpering.

I don't remember much, but something was coming.

Something —

And so: we were going to open BEATRICE (CENCI) AND THE OLD MAN. It was very well Directed, by Wendy Chapin, and well Cast.

From the Journal of Sands Hall
July 1978, Lexington

Opening of BEATRICE last night. Went well, I suppose. I am not sure if anyone exterior to the company "got it," this troubling play billed as "A BIZARRE COMEDY" — but then, what is the message? That we must Kill the Parent? (All through the rehearsals I've dealt with this.) What does he mean when he says to Kate: "I am Beatrice. I am Beatrice and Theodore." He adds: "She is stronger than I am. She does what I never could do." What does he *mean*? That God punishes us for ingratitude? That God, in the end, loves us?

Is all life a travesty for Oakley? Is the play a message? A declaration of war? All questions. No answers? Even that is a question.

Well, it deals with huge themes. I wonder if Shakespeare's plays had opening nights and such responses to King Lear or whatever.

The love for him abounds. Who knows what this play will mean tonight, with the audience composed not of friends willing to laugh and promote both play and actors, but one that is there to see "A BIZARRE COMEDY." And probably a small house, too.

Freddy, the bartender, filled with wisdom about the dare it takes for a man to put his SELF up on a platform for everybody to look at and point fingers to. And that he is a little crazy, too, and that he, Freddy, understands that craziness. "Just got to let him do it. He'll be alright. He's the most alright person I know."

Dr. David M. Levine, MD
Massachusetts General Hospital

Oakley Hall is a 28-year-old right-handed married playwright and novelist. On July 17ᵗʰ he fell 30 feet off a bridge onto a rock quarry, injuring his head and face. He was taken to a local hospital in Stamford, New York, where a tracheotomy was inserted and he was transferred that night to the Albany Medical Center. There, he had a splenectomy and was followed for two to three weeks by a team of neurosurgeons, though no neurosurgical procedures were carried out. His wife reports that he seemed to be conscious in that he was moving and responding within two to three days after the accident. The patient, however, has had a period of post-traumatic amnesia, lasting at least 5 weeks.

Sands's Journal:

Monday, at 1 AM the phone rang. Sue Bedsoe, up in Lexington saying, "Your brother's had an accident." From what she said it did not sound serious but that he had been taken to the hospital.

Waited for a confirming call from Lexington. Finally called them. Not good news. Transferred from

Stamford to Albany. Sigrid said to walk up and tell Mary. They did not want to call her — fear of the baby she carries.

Oddly, I felt no apprehension. A large whack on the head, perhaps? But I ran up thru the rain to the phone booth below Mary and Oakley's apartment. Called. She seemed to know something was up. Before I said anything: "What's happened? Is he OK?"

Dr. Ballantine
Massachusetts General

Impression on Admission was cerebral trauma with multiple cerebral contusions. CT scan showed a resolution of haematoma; increasing and persistent attenuation zone in the left frontal lobe suggesting necrosis.

<u>Sands's Journal</u>:

Somehow I could deal with Oakley alive or dead — that choice made. But when it emerged — the possibility of brain damage — my brother not — My mind skittered. In addition to the fact that he fell on his head, there is the possibility he stopped breathing between Lexington and Stamford Hospital, where the tracheotomy was inserted. The nurse, to quote, said, "Oh hell, another D.O.A." She was fired the next day.

Dr. Ballantine

Massachusetts General

CT Scan

The patient is identified as having multiple calvarial fractures. There is fracture in the left frontal area with a questionable fracture in the base of the skull as identified with fluid density in the sphenoid sinus. There is a fracture in the right sphenoid wing. There is a fracture in the left lamina papyracea with bony fragments identified in the retrobulbar area. There is probable elevation with fracture in the roof of the right orbit. There is extraconal swelling in the left orbit .

<u>Sands</u>:

I get to the studio at CBS — my first day shooting on THE GUIDING LIGHT, *of all things* — at 7 AM. The incredible HAVE to go to work. Then a phone call from Sofia saying, "He's in a coma. Michael thinks you should be there. Your mom and dad are flying out." It was that last detail that sent me into a total PANIC. It was *serious*.

Apparently I dove off the Bridge that I used to walk across to get to the Bar. A long way down, I remember 42 feet.

And my peculiar, almost Joyful state when I hit bottom.

I landed on a Big Boulder. I remember the warm, Liquid feeling of bleeding. I remember . . . Peace.

Hume found me. I was bleeding, almost Dead.

And, as I remember, Happy.

That's how I remember it.

<u>Sands</u>:

Monday, July 24th, Albany Hospital

This — thing — in a white hospital bed. What shall I describe first? The huge head, 2-1/2 times its size, unrecognizable but for those full lips, the stringy hair sliding away from bandaged forehead. Instead of eyes two slices of Santa Rosa plums puff an inch above eye sockets. The tube attached to the inside of his nose whose inner nostrils are still coated with blood. The tracheotomy protrudes from his throat, the thick bull throat his neck has become. Dried blood all around this as well. On his chest are taped wires and bandages and metal gadgets. Out of each of his arms tangle what look like a million tubes. On his chest from breast to pelvis a bandage four inches wide covers bailing stitches which still bleed slightly. From his penis, yet another tube, filled with urine and colored red with blood. Bottles hang and drip viscous liquid into tubes running towards him, out of him come tubes filled with grey and pink matter. A wind machine sits on the floor and expands a collapsed lung with a whooshing sound. To the left of the bed is a machine with little flashing lights wheezing as it assists him to breathe. When the trach snaps out of his throat it makes a rattling sound of lost breath which warns everybody that he is without air. On the other side of the bed squats another machine, with a window and yellow lights — his heartbeat, steady, steady thank goodness the little bouncing ball up . . . up . . . up. Breathing.

I remember, distinctly, during the Accident, going to a Boston Hospital (I was then at the bottom of the Bridge in Lexington, New York), nude, walking through doors 'cause I was Dead, going to a room and finding there a glass of White Wine, and an unmarked Camel Cigarette. I picked them both up and went to the window, where a section of Boston lay, White, before me.

I was nude, White, White Wine and Camel Cigarette, White, and Boston. I remember, basically, White.

At that moment in my memory, Michael Hume knew, sensed, that I had not made it back.

Merdre.

<u>Sands</u>:

So I head back to New York. The TOTAL ridiculousness of going to a Soap Opera! putting make-up on my face, learning lines, watching for light angles and the red lit bulb on Camera 1 with the pressure of this knowledge on my mind . . . .

Three worst days of my life. Then back up to Albany Friday. O so much improved I burst into tears. Looking like himself — a miracle. Yes. Eyes a little open, still horribly puffy, nodding. In Oakley-exasperation pulling out his catheter, his I.V.s, his tubes, at the one in his nose. Unable to understand what the fuck is going on. I try to put myself somewhere near where he must be. In what fog of understanding between sleeping and waking he must be lying.

<u>Dr. Levine</u>:

He was transferred to the Mass. General Hospital three weeks after his accident. His wife recalls that on admission he appeared to be very lethargic, quiet, and somewhat indifferent. He appeared to recognize his wife. He spoke in full sentences but often did not make much sense. After three weeks he was transferred to the Mass Eye and Ear for surgery on his face.

Sands:

Saturday night went to Lexington to see the last performance of BEATRICE AND THE OLD MAN. This play which asks all these questions of God and Man and their relationship to one another. Not a good performance. All spirit, all humor gone, attention on Oakley in the hospital, the significance of it all.

The night of the accident, Patrick, Sue Bedsoe's boyfriend, had a huge pull to the place under the Bridge after all the activity was gone. Was down there scrabbling about long after. "There's something here Oakley wants, I can feel it." Sue says "ESP" and talks of psychic energy. Perhaps I agree. She got Patrick to go to bed and he felt the pull all night. In the morning back down below the bridge he found Oakley's derby, completely accordioned. He punched the brim back into shape, dusted it off. I wonder if it broke his fall. He does love it — wears it always.

Pure Jarry.

Ran into Dr. Steven Bock and wife Jeanine. I could say nothing. Tears in my eyes, I held out a hand. The man who saved Oakley's life. Literally. Pushing at the inert body in the Stamford Hospital, practically beating him up, "Don't you die you bastard get back here you mother-fucker." Puncturing the throat with no attention to cosmetic detail, just getting the tracheotomy in there so that breath would activate the essential parts of his body again.

I remember waking to extreme pain, on the table at Dr. Bock's house. "I saved your life," said Steve Bock later. "Several times."

"Yeah," I slurred, not having full control over my mouth. "But I was quite happy being Dead."

"Ah, well." He shrugged. "I'm a Doctor. Doctors Preserve Life."

And cigarettes — that's funny and horrible. He dives for them across the room, sees a butt and matches, sticks it in his mouth. There the white stub sits above the hole in his throat.

I don't remember any of this at all.

Michael Stillwell, a man who'd been hanging around the company for a week or so, was drinking with Oakley at the Lexington Bar the night of the accident, and he said they were walking back across the Bridge and Oakley said something about feeling aggressive. Stillwell says he said, "Why don't you not take it out on people? Take it out on the bridge?" and he grabbed a girder and started shaking it, half-laughing. And he said Oakley grabbed the edge of the bridge with two hands — the railing — as if he were going to "jump it like a tennis net." What did he intend? I don't know. "I think he must have just lost it," Stillwell said. "I saw his left hand trail off and then heard a plop, like he'd landed in water, or mud."

My vision fills with what that fall must have been filled with for Oakley. What thoughts? Relief? Letting go?

Oh my God? Expectation he would get wet in the water? Shock? Dead? Thoughts of Mary, of LCT? Of drinking? How many things flashed through his mind before his body hit?

Stillwell says he ran down. Out waist deep in the water, couldn't find him. Thought he'd fallen in the water and sunk. Frantic. Then heard him breathing, gurgling. In total blackness felt his way towards the sound. Checked, Boy Scout like, all his bones. Found his face covered, not with water but with something warm, something sticky, blood. Turned him on his side and RAN, found Sigrid and James Rice and Hume in the canteen and they were ON it, immediately. Within seconds the Lexington rescue squad was there. (That too a wonder: this tiny town inhabited by descendants of Lithuanian immigrants, some seemingly inbred descendents of Rip Van Winkle, mad neighbors down the side roads, a small artistic community; how did they have a rescue team so drilled and ready? And how was it that Sigrid was taking a class in CPR and so knew what to do, who to call?)

"So weird, Sands," Hume said. "The night was so black and these huge white lights beaming down, whiting everything out, except for the black of the river and of the earth and then this red of blood on his face. And as they were getting him up, rain began to fall."

Heavens crying.

I don't remember who Michael Stillwell is.

In my memory, I was alone.

It had been a drinking-oriented night, celebration of the end of the Opening Weekend: BEATRICE was up and running.

I either fell from the bridge, jumped, or was hurled.

There was very little water in the creek. Which I knew very, very well.

It may have been a Suicide Attempt.

I don't know in fact, if it was an Accident, a Suicide Attempt, an Attempted Murder. I also Can't figure out Who would want me Dead.

Or Why I would want to kill myself.

<u>Dr. Levine</u>:

The patient feels that since his accident he has had a sense of "man being in combat with himself." He talks of hallucinations but it is unclear that he is having actual abnormal perceptual experiences instead of merely an attitude or sense that he is being persecuted.

The patient's wife reports that he "sees men in trees with rifles after him." While she acknowledges that he had paranoid tendencies, both in his general behavior as well as in his writings, prior to his accident, she feels that his behavior is atypical in the increased intensity of his paranoia. He is considerably more obsessive than normal. Before bed he checks his clothing and the bed for bugs. He must make sure all the doors are closed and the windows are locked. He is also most particular about his food. Formally a big eater, he is now "nitpickily negative" and highly critical of his food. He appears very restless as well. He states that he is eager to get back to New York and begin a book but in Plymouth, although a typewriter is available, has made no attempt to write.

I spent Ten Months in Five Hospitals, from Albany to Boston.

I came out of it with an I.Q. of 6.

It was one of those head-injuries one hears about occasionally, where you live, but you are never quite the same.

Dr. Levine:

On examination the patient is alert and affable . . . His speech is fluent and not paraphasic, although he clearly has difficulties in expressing himself precisely. On one occasion when putting on his shoes he looked carefully into each. When asked why, he said, "I'm checking the inside for flies." Asked why he did this he said, "I have something in my heels." Asked what that might be he said, "I don't know, sphagnum or something." He was unable to explain the word. On another occasion he was asked what an orange and a banana have in common and his answer was "You can make frappes of them both." Asked to elucidate what the proverb, "One swallow does not a summer make" meant he said, "Well, you can interpret it two ways: swallow might refer to a bird or it could refer to a delicious swallow of beer."

After the Accident, when I drank, I got drunk fast.

Very, very fast.

As I remember it.

I had the Accident for a Reason. I just don't know What it Was.

Dr. Levine:

Thank you very much for referring this most interesting patient.

I went on living in New York City, same apartment, with my Wife and Newborn Son, Oakley Maxwell Hall IV.

I remember I spent the first five years thinking Meg, my wife, was a Nurse from the hospital.

This was Unfortunate.

And Wrong.

I do remember the day O-Four was born. Meg was quite pregnant, and one day she said, "Well, it's time."

We went out, me holding her somewhat, flagged a cab and went to our Hospital, which wasn't really very far away. As I recall she delivered very fast, but there was a shortage of Nurses, and I held O-Four, still wet and bloody.

I remember his speaking to me, that first day. He was thrust into my arms, all Wet and Bloody. He looked at me with humorous eyes, and said, "Hi, Dad."

I also remember him getting me out of Bars in Manhattan.

I think he was too young.

We are, meanwhile, getting very, very low on Money.

We switch from Absinthe to Ether. My, my, this is alarming. We don't go out much anymore, we lie at home, wracked with headaches, and Giggling occasionally. It is a change, though not a good one.

In my absence, and I was absent from the end of the first week of BEATRICE (CENCI) AND THE OLD MAN for two and a half years, the Company worked as it worked. It probably worked fine.

I have heard from a local source, who didn't know me at the time, that everything got a lot more "plastic" after I was Ambulanced away. This is an actual quote, "Plastic."

I am not sure I understand, but I might.

More "Summerstocky."

I had already laid out the next Summer's Plays, or most of them.

Lexington Conservatory Theatre moved to Albany, New York. This seemed okay to me, though I wouldn't have allowed the Raise in Rent which threw us out of Lexington.

Michael van Landingham found an abandoned Safeway for the Theatre. The building was all-right built and had in it an amazing Sound System.

As I remember.

Since we were no longer in Lexington, the name was changed: Capital Repertory. We were the first Equity theatre — theatre that used mostly Union actors — in Albany, or so I heard.

And Meg and O-Four and I moved to Albany.

It was, to me, Dull. I remember, vaguely, dark alleys.

And all the kids who had interned at Lexington now had rank over me, in a Theatre I had co-founded and that I used to run.

I didn't Artistic Direct, or Assistant Artistic Direct, or do anything for the Theatre in Albany, I think Vano thought I was Mentally Short.

And he was right.

I went to live with our sister, Charlotte, 13 rue Charles-Landelle. We would get dressed in our Fashionable togs and sit outside at Café tables, occasionally sniffing Ether. We had hallucinations that lasted days. It was not Fun. Interesting for writing? Maybe. But not Fun.

I eventually wound up in Squaw Valley, where my parents still live. Mary and O-Four were with me for a while, and then she . . . Split.

Our body hurts at odd moments. Is this a sign of Age? We hope not.

We are, after all, only about twenty-eight. That is not old. But We feel, each morning, each time We saunter down the street, that We are Old.

In Squaw Valley I got a telephone call from Bruce Bouchard, who had taken over Capital Rep, as Artistic Director.

One: he wanted my congratulations. He got them.

Two: he wanted to know who I would recommend to replace Vano as Company-runner, Executive Director. I could think of no one but Peter Clough, who had in my vague memory, run a theatre in Maine or somewhere and I suggested him.

Three: he wanted to do my FRANKENSTEIN again. I said Fine.

I went. It was kind of fine. Different Cast. I was, for some reason, bored. Actually, I know the reason. FRANKENSTEIN at LCT had been a group effort. At Capital Rep, as directed by Clough, there was no sense of Finding the Play, finding the Drama, finding the Life in Frankenstein's Monster, no sense of Rooting for Him.

Frankenstein's MONSTER was bigger, though.

But not as good as Hume.

I saw Sofia Landon while I was there. She had divorced van Landingham. She looked Sweet, as always. She gave me a hug.

"You look good," she said, looked at me, steadily. "Do you remember our conversation about Jarry?"

I nodded. I did remember.

"Well, you did it," she said, "you actually pulled it off. And you're still Living!"

"Barely," I said.

I got so close to Dying in LaValle that they gave me the Last Rites. I made out a Will, leaving everything to Mme Rachilde.

That was May 28. So few people showed up to Mourn for Us, like Three, that We got better, and on the 26th of July, moved back to Paris. After all, we were Alfred Jarry, the UBU-meister. Three people at UBU's Death?

We went to Paris so we could die with more Glory. And of course, Paris is Paris.

Dr. Bonnie E. Durandetto:

Psychological and Neuropsychological Assessment Psychotherapy. January 30, 1986

At the time of his injury, seven years ago, Oakley Hall III had been successfully building up a theatre company he called the Lexington Conservatory Theatre. Whereas he seems to show no drive at present, prior to his accident he seemed almost "driven" in that he was so active and, at times, impatient.

Oakley drinks and is now unable to tolerate alcohol such that he has episodes he cannot remember later. He also has terrifying nightmares to the extent that he needs to have someone with him.

Oakley is primarily concerned about his constant fears. For example, he is afraid of being around windows (someone might look in or even shoot him). He used to be afraid of finding bugs everywhere. While these and other fears continue, they have lessened somewhat. His fears are of such severity that he sometimes wishes he could have "a pill to put me to sleep . . . to ease the fear." He denies active suicidal thoughts or plans, however. In assessing the nature and quality of Oakley's fears and terrors, it is important to note that at the same time he is experiencing these acute fears, which limit his life in very significant ways, he has the ability to understand and comment on the fact that they are not "real."

This did not make them any less terrifying.

Dr. Durandetto:

Oakley is concerned about his lack of drive and initiative. He wonders if he will ever have the initiative to even work part time. At the same time that he is concerned about this change in himself, he experiences a lack of strong concern or worry about it. As a matter of fact this lack of concern concerns him.

He scored very high on an entrance examination for a graduate program in English Literature and was accepted into a graduate program at U.C. Davis. However, he was unable to tolerate attending classes and stopped attending.

My mother helped me get into the University of California, Davis, as a grad. student. I was, at this point, a pretty bad drunk, and she got me in, found me a place to live, in hopes of saving me. I remember Davis as a small town, off the Freeway, with few shops and few places that sold alcohol.

I spoke with the Secretary in Charge of the Ph.D. Program, and she said I would need three years' work on Grammar to qualify for my PhD. This did not sound good to me. I found a bar on the Main Drag, called The Club. I loved its clients. They served three drinks: a Draft beer, no title to it; a Draft White wine, without a name; and a Bourbon. It had a name, I just didn't know it.

I started drinking there. It had the advantage, in case I couldn't sleep, of opening at six in the morning and closing at four in the morning.

I re-met Robin Campbell, whom I'd met before at the Squaw Valley Writer's Conference, and we went to a party of Gay people. It was a lot of fun, and I stayed the night with her.

She had an old car, and a middle-finger ring that she tapped on the steering wheel. She was quite good-looking too.

The next morning I woke up at her place and noticed a tremendous number of dishes, which I asked her about. She said she bought new/used dishes at garage sales in order to Not Do Dishes.

So I set myself the plan of doing All Her Dishes for her.

Meanwhile ignoring Class Schedules.

And I did them, too. We had a lot of dishes we didn't use, after that. But you could use the Sink. This was the start of my Almost-Compulsive Dishwashing.

After that I got a job, from the son of the Man who owned The Club, tending bar there. It wasn't very hard. Beer, you tapped, cost 75 cents. Wine, you tapped, cost 75 cents; Bourbon, you poured into a Guest-In-Motel-Room-Glass, cost One Dollar. It was easy to remember.

And Paris is debts. I owed a lot. I owed so much I could have, if I'd ever had the Money, bought Paris, and turned it into a Ubique Resort. UBU Walking flat-footed around, with Mme Rachilde and so forth.

Although I am having a more difficult time getting either Mme Rachilde or her husband Vallette to talk to me, or walk with me.

Ether is making me a lot less Sociable. I Hate everything, and this Giggle is driving me nuts.

From my beautiful blonde friend, Ramona Moon, whom I'd met at Irvine and was a playwright at Lexington, Robin and I were offered a place to live: her father's old place in Worthington, Ohio.

Worthington's a suburb of Columbus. The house was suburban, but its back yard was a Park, so it was open, Friendly.

A Theatre Company in Columbus, called REALITY THEATRE, was having a New Play Contest, and I submitted a Play I had written at Lexington, but had no expectation of ever seeing done, called A DYING ART. The Reality Theatre liked it, chose it to win, and did it.

It was strange to have another Theatre Company doing the show.

One that I had No Control over.

The Reality Theatre also did a staged reading of BEATRICE (CENCI) AND THE OLD MAN.

This was also strange, and got an Audience Response.

Basically positive, but as if I were a New Playwright.

It was in a sense a Comeback into the Theatre.

But I went back to being With Myself. To talking endlessly about things in the Theatre that I Liked, or Had Done.

Remembering.

Drunk, and Remembering.

What I remember is moments. Moments of a particular kind of joy, of loveliness.

Moments of Hume, where you direct him wrong, and he gets it right from some Interior Knowledge; Zobel, the unknowing Heavy of our Theatre Company, with his moustache; Wendy Chapin, the girl who smiles politely, and can fix anything in your theatre, and is a pretty good Director, too.

Remembering: Drunk and Stoned and having the unquestionable Power of an Artistic Director. Except the Power is not Unquestionable, it's Very Questionable, and gets Questioned quite a bit.

Remembering having friends like Bouchard and Nisbet, and even Sofia Landon. She set up the Women's League of Theatre Artists, because she felt that women were not getting enough attention from the Artistic Director. And she could be right.

Nisbet was a handsome man literally rotting because LTA/LCT didn't do something. I thought about that at the time and didn't know what to do.

And Bouchard was a Loose Cannon. Running about all over the place, making at first minor, then more and more major changes in Actor Reality. When LCT moved to Albany in 1980, and became Capital Repertory, Bruce came out of retirement as a Bond Seller, and when Michael van Landingham got bumped by the Mayor of Albany, Bouchard took over as Artistic Director.

Maybe he now knows. Knows what I remember.

Remembering the months of work. Remembering the Shaping of a Play. Remembering finding the Moment, or Sequence of Moments, the Build. Remembering Opening Nights, in Lexington, in New York City. Remembering absurd and very violent quarrels.

And that is all I can do. Remember . . ..

We were having a difficult time breathing, and in January of 1906 We went back to Charlotte. She had left 13 Rue Charles-Landell for 13 Rue du Bootz. It was our Ancestral Home.

I continued to write. I bought some Absinthe.

We went back to Paris.

Worthington, Ohio, is Worthington. And Columbus is Columbus. I remember the Absolute Beauty of Nature there. I went to work for the Worthington Public Library, reshelving Books that had been Returned.

This was about the Maximum that I was capable of. And I loved it.

This was a curious thing that came after My Accident. Loving Things. Before, I had just tolerated them. Now I Loved Them.

We — Robin and I — stayed in Worthington for three years, and then got a truck, filled it with all our stuff, and moved to Random Lake, Wisconsin.

Random Lake. Great name.

To live with her old high-school friend Scott Karstenson, who owned a house there.

And I got a job working at the one factory in Random Lake.

I worked the Twilight Shift: 2 in the afternoon to 10, and then it was beer-time. I didn't mind the work, and I liked my co-worker, Rick, a lot. He was quite amazing to watch drink, in one of the nine bars in a town with a population of maybe two hundred. A beer every couple of minutes. He had no Driver's License, it had been pulled, and he spent about half the year in Prison, in a cell called Rick's Cell. I also loved the fact that Wisconsin had a real life, heavy-duty political party called the Socialists. of which Rick was one.

I was writing in the mornings.

UBU CUCKOLDED doesn't work as a Play, and We were working at making it more UBIQUE.

We felt a spasm, and another.

We lost the motion in our legs. We lay there for two days, hoping someone would come by. It was Vallette, for the first time in a while, and Dr. Saltas. They took Us to Hospital. The Hospital of Charity. We lay there for a long time, became obsessed, with, well, a Toothpick.

Robin and I stayed three years in Random Lake. Then we broke up, and I migrated from there to my sister Tracy's house in Colorado. I met, or re-met, Tracy's kids: Justin, Nico, and Emma.

We fixed up Tracy's house, which she had bought in a terminal state, and I moved out back, to a shed. I made it mine.

I put the Scissors I had made for UBU, long and painted black, in the front window.

Just a reminder of Lexington Conservatory Theatre.

In a Life that did not remind me too much of it.

We asked for a toothpick. It was brought to Us.

We lay there, with the Toothpick in our mouth, and blissfully thanked them.

Then We Died.

November 1, at 4:15 PM.

All Saints' Day, of course.

We left a will leaving everything to Mme Rachilde.

I loved Absinthe. It did wonders for my Antic Qualities.

Very Slow to get made, very bad tasting, the Gate to UBU.

Those who reminisce about me, Toulouse-Lautrec, Alfred Vallette, and so forth, all remark on my gaiety, combined with a dead-pan face.

That was Ubique. The total-seeming control, of a very out of control situation. That was UBU. That was Absinthe.

Absinthe took me Early to My Death.

Do I object?

No, I don't think so. It was a Life.

I, Oakley Hall III, had a life. It was, perhaps, not as wonderful as Jarry's, but it had its moments.

And I have one still. Not as rich or as together as it was, as I could have had. I didn't have Absinthe, didn't have the Docturds saying, after I was dead, that I looked A Hundred Years Old, inside. I think that Jarry died at the right time for Him.

I think.

We were Dead.

As was, I suppose, I.

Merdre.

Jarry dies with a grin on his face. Classic.

I, eventually, moved to Nevada City, where I now live. My I.Q. has improved somewhat since the accident.

I, too, have a grin on my face.

I didn't die. And therefore the two stories, Mine and Jarry's, don't match exactly.

But the I of Me did die.

It is curious to be here in Paris. It's much more Modern, now. But there are still evidences of Us, and of Our Time.

And that's Good.

We suppose.

Merdre.

Merdre.

Alfred Jarry in 1896, the year of *Ubu Roi*'s première
Photographed by Nadar (Gaspard-félix Tournachon)

PLAYS BY OAKLEY HALL III:

DOORMAN

MIKE FINK

FRANKENSTEIN
(based on the 1869 novel by Mary Shelley)

GRINDER'S STAND

BEATRICE (CENCI) AND THE OLD MAN
(based loosely on 1935 play THE CENCI by Antonin Artaud, in turn based loosely on the works of Percy Bysshe Shelley and Henri B. Stendhal)

UNPRODUCED PLAYS:

MELMOTH THE WANDERER
(based on the 1820 novel by Charles Robert Maturin)

THE MONKS OF MONK HALL
(based on the 1845 novel by George Lippard)

THE MOONSTONE
(based on the 1871 novel by Wilkie Collins)

THE OCCULTATION AND LUMIFICATION OF MR. UBU

Above: The author and his *chérie*, Hadiya Wilborn, in 2010.
Photo by Tom Taylor

EDITOR'S NOTE

When I read an early draft of this book, I believed, as Oakley Hall III obliquely asserts in his introductory material, that at some time during the 1970s he had found Alfred Jarry's handwritten autobiography at a yard sale in upstate New York, in a sack of loose papers.

Less skeptical than the unbelievers who asked Joseph Smith if they might view and touch the golden plates from which he claimed to have translated the *Book of Mormon*, I asked Oakley if he still possessed Jarry's original material. Could the crumbling, absinthe-stained pages be languishing under the floor of his mother's study in her house at Squaw Valley, California, in the narrow basement that houses her archival photographs of legendary writers? If we could have the handwritten autobiography authenticated, in addition to its considerable value in helping me prepare the manuscript for publication, the damned thing would be worth a fortune.

As Oakley feinted, parried and thrust concerning the whereabouts of his yard-sale find, the truth intruded on my fantasies: Although drawing upon the assorted writings of Jarry and his contemporaries, *Oakley essentially made this all up!* When I asked directly, he readily confirmed my suspicion with an Ubique chuckle.

A family friend of the Halls once described Oakley to me as "the original unreliable narrator." Mindful of this, I circled every questionable assertion that I found during my subsequent read-through. And what did this latter-day skeptic learn during the ensuing research? That *Bar-Snister* and *'Pataphysics* are not typographical errors. That, although Jarry did suffer from tuberculosis, he legitimately can be said to have "died of too much absinthe," as Oakley claims. And that, consistent with my suspicions, Oakley Hall III is every bit as interesting a character, and writer, as Alfred Jarry.

Steve Susoyev

We have made every effort to attribute accurately the photographs and quotations used in this volume. Several archival photographs not otherwise credited were used by permission of the EVERGREEN REVIEW, and reproduced from Volume 4, Number 13 of that publication (May-June 1960). The print version of the EVERGREEN REVIEW ceased publication in 1973, but the magazine was revived in 1998 in an online edition, at www.EvergreenReview.com.
Please let the editors know of anything we have missed, so that we may make appropriate corrections in future editions.
You may contact us at Editor@MovingFingerPress.com. Thank you.

The Loss of Nameless Things
A Film by Bill Rose

"A documentary as eloquent as its title."

Kevin Thomas, *Los Angeles Times*

Distributed on DVD by PBS Home Video
Available through Amazon.com, Netflix, ITUNES and ShopPBS

Documentary filmmaker Bill Rose examines the tragic fall from grace of the playwright whom many critics believed to be the next great voice in American theater. When Oakley Hall III fell from a bridge not far from the Lexington Conservatory Theater in 1978, both his life and career were irreparably altered, leaving many to wonder what would become of the man whom critics often singled out as an *enfant terrible* with an incredibly bright future. Flash forward twenty-five years, and Hall III was hired as a playwright and consultant by a Northern California theater troupe determined to stage the play that he was writing the night that his life was forever changed, providing filmmaker Rose with the ideal opportunity to bring his remarkable story to the screen.

Jason Buchanan, *All Movie Guide*

Absintheur Press
San Francisco
WWW.ABSINTHEURPRESS.COM
Absintheur Press is an Ubique division of Moving Finger Press

ALSO AVAILABLE FROM MOVING FINGER PRESS:

Tools of the Writer's Craft by Sands Hall

"Reading this book is like learning how a juggler juggles. It will be invaluable for writers new and old, and for anyone giving or taking a writing workshop."

Lynn Freed, author of
The Curse of the Appropriate Man

Return to the Caffe Cino
edited by Steve Susoyev and George Birimisa

Winner of the 2007 Lambda Literary Foundation Book Award
for Theater & Drama

"Obviously a labor of love and an amazing and important work."

New York Public Library
for the Performing Arts at Lincoln Center

People Farm by Steve Susoyev

"A profound and ethically challenging tale of desperation... Confounds the issue of morality by offering no easy answers to the question of how far one should be willing to go to find acceptance, love, and inner peace... and reminds us of the corruptibility of good intentions."

The Gay and Lesbian Review Worldwide

Moving Finger Press

San Francisco
www.MovingFingerPress.com

Printed in the United States
by United Graphics of Mattoon, Illinois

Book and cover design by Steve Susoyev